HENRY HOLT EDITIONS IN PSYCHOLOGY

CLEVER HANS

CLEVER HANS

(THE HORSE OF MR. VON OSTEN)

By
Oskar Pfungst

Edited by
Robert Rosenthal
Harvard University

A HENRY HOLT EDITION
IN PSYCHOLOGY

HOLT, RINEHART AND WINSTON, INC.
NEW YORK · CHICAGO · SAN FRANCISCO
TORONTO · LONDON

CONTENTS

PREFACE

There was a time when the case of Clever Hans was widely read and widely cited. In recent years, however, Hans has been relegated more and more to the footnotes of scholarly treatises with only rare exceptions. (Two such recent exceptions are to be found in Brown [1958] and in Polanyi [1958].) This relegation has been an unfortunate loss, abetted no doubt by the unavailability of the book. Students, and particularly students of psychology, should have the opportunity to read the case of Clever Hans, and they should read it for what it is—a case study of scientific method applied to a fascinating theoretical and practical problem. They will recognize that only a very small part of the value of the book stems from the fact that it is a "remarkable tale of credulity founded on unconscious deceit," as Angell described it. Now here it is, available again, this time as part of an important series, and published by the same firm, plus two, that issued the original 1911 translation. They must be thanked for permitting Hans to tap again.

The research which prompted the careful reconsideration of the case of Clever Hans, only a portion of which is described here, has been supported by the Division of Social Sciences of the National Science Foundation (G-17685, G-24826, GS-177). I am grateful to William Dember for his encouragement, and to Claire Fishman, Neil Friedman, Daniel Kurland, and especially Theodore Newcomb for their valuable comments on an earlier draft. My greatest debt in the preparation of this Introduction is to E. G. Boring for his scholarship, wisdom, and kindness.

Robert Rosenthal

Cambridge, Massachusetts
June 1965

INTRODUCTION

Clever Hans: A Case Study of Scientific Method

ROBERT ROSENTHAL
Harvard University

I

Ever since the Byzantine Empire was ruled by Justinian (A.D. 483–565) there have been reports of learned animals. But no animal intelligence so captured the imagination of layman and scholar alike as that attributed to Clever Hans, the horse of Mr. von Osten. Hans gave every evidence of being able to add and subtract, multiply and divide—operations performed with equal accuracy upon integers or fractions. He was also able to read and spell, to identify musical tones, and to state the relationship of tones to one another. His preferred mode of communication with his questioners was by means of converting all answers into a number and tapping out these numbers with his foot.

What Clever Hans and Mr. von Osten did for science (and for love), Clever Rosa, the mare of Berlin, and her owner did for entertainment (and for money). Any expert on animal training could observe that Rosa's behavior was under the strict control of her trainer. Rosa gave correct answers because her trainer had only to bend forward in order to stop her tapping at the correct point, but no such signals could be observed to control Hans's tapping responses. In fact, on September 12, 1904, thirteen men risked their professional reputations by certifying that Hans was receiving no intentional cues from his owner or from any other questioner. Furthermore, these men, including in their number a psychologist, a physiologist, a veterinarian, a director of the Berlin Zoo, and a circus manager, certified that their investigation revealed no presence of signs or cues of even an unintentional nature. "This is a case," the investigating committee wrote, "which appears in principle to differ from any hitherto discovered." A "serious and incisive" inquiry into the cleverness of Hans was recommended and subsequently conducted. This book is the report by Oskar Pfungst of the procedure and the results of that inquiry which was undertaken in collaboration with Carl Stumpf, the eminent psychologist.[1]

Clever Hans constitutes a famous "case" in the history of psychology. One wishes to know about it for its own sake. There is, however, another reason for reprinting this book, long so difficult to obtain. The investigation of Hans's abilities is also a classic in respect of method, for it is a first-rate scientific inquiry into what began as an incomprehensible case history.

Pfungst's work is ideal as a paradigm for this kind of inquiry. First, he did careful and sophisticated work. Second, he described his procedures and his thinking in such detail that anyone, layman or student, can understand what goes on in a scientific inquiry. Third, the subject of his investigation has great intrinsic interest.[2]

First Pfungst established that Hans was, in fact, clever, and that his cleverness did not depend on the presence of his master, Mr. von Osten. Anyone, or almost anyone, could put a question to Hans, and the chances were good that an accurate answer would be forthcoming. Next, Pfungst employed a control condition in fitting Hans with blinders so that he could not see his questioners. This experimental addition reduced Hans's cleverness. There was another experimental change that cramped Hans's style: The questioners asked questions to which they did not know the answers. Pfungst also noted that Hans's accuracy diminished as the physical distance between him and his questioners increased. The closer the questioner, the more impressive was Hans's performance. From these data Pfungst could see that Hans was clever only when he had visual access to a source of the correct answer. In this indirect manner the likelihood had been increased that visual cues were involved, despite the fact that no specific visual cues had as yet been discovered.[3]

Eventually Pfungst noticed that the slight forward inclination of the questioner's head, to better see Hans's hoof tapping, was the signal for Hans to begin tapping. This forward inclination of the head did not need to be accompanied by a question for it to serve as a stimulus to tapping by Hans. When a correct answer required a long series of taps Hans would tap at a faster rate, as though he knew he had a lot of work ahead of him. This accommodation to the task at hand, which greatly added to the intellectual status ascribed to Hans, also came to be understood by Pfungst: He found that the interrogator, when putting a question to Hans, tended to lean further forward when the number that was the answer was a large one—as though he were settling down for a long wait. Hans's rate of tapping apparently depended on the angle of the questioner's forward inclination. Similarly, the cue for Hans to stop tapping also turned out to be derived from the questioner's expectancy for a correct answer; for when Hans reached the correct number of taps, the questioner tended to straighten up—and that was the cue for Hans to stop. Hans was sensitive to tiny upward motions of the head, even to the raising of eyebrows or the dilation of nostrils, any of which was sufficient to stop his tapping. Pfungst showed that anyone could start Hans tapping, and that anyone else could then stop his tapping at any time by the use of these cues. Most interesting was the finding that even after he had learned the cueing system very well Pfungst still cued Hans unintentionally, though he was consciously trying to suppress sending the crucial visual messages.

When Pfungst had learned all this about this man-horse communication system, he did a very modern thing indeed. He took his discoveries to the laboratory for further confirmation. As he put it, "Thus, artificial synthesis became the test of the correctness of analytical observation." In order to increase the generality of his findings at this point he not only increased his sample size but sampled from a different species —people, instead of horses. Pfungst took the part of Hans, inviting questions to which he tapped out his answers.

Of 25 subjects, 23 unintentionally cued Pfungst as to when he should stop tapping! When errors did occur, they tended to be errors of either one too many or one too few taps—the kind of errors Hans was most likely to make. The subjects, including men and women of assorted ages and occupations, had of course not been told the intent of the experiment. One of the subjects was a psychologist trained in introspection, but even he was unable to discover that he was emitting cues to Pfungst, Hans's surrogate.

To record his subjects' responses permanently and for leisurely study, as well as to amplify their very subtle cues, Pfungst developed an ingenious system of instrumentation. The questioner-subjects were hooked into a series of recording devices which would record an amplification of their head movements on three planes. In addition he undertook to measure the changes in his subjects' respiration. In interpreting the results of these recordings, Pfungst postulated a build-up of tension in his subjects that was released as a motor response to the perception of the correct answer as the experimenter tapped it out.

II

Pfungst's findings solved not only the riddle of Clever Hans but in principle the problem of other "clever" animals. Now there was a reasonable explanation available for the ability of Hugo Kretschmer's dog to answer questions by means of pressing a bell. Similarly, the abilities of the English bulldog "Kepler" of Sir William Huggins could be better understood. Kepler barked the answers to problems put to him, just as Hans had tapped them out. It seemed only reasonable to assume that by some tone or movement Sir William started Kepler's clever barking, and then by some other subtle movement stopped his dog's barking at the number of barks that were correct. Most of the other clever animals of that time were never so mysterious because their cueing was obvious, and often obviously intentional. That was the case with Hans's vaudeville rival, Rosa, the mare of Berlin. Similar mechanisms seemed to operate in the clever dog of Utrecht, the reading pig of London, and the reading pig and talking horse of Virginia.[4,5]

In his Preface to the present volume, James R. Angell mentioned its relevance to the then current wave of interest in animal life and behavior—a relevance that is, if anything, even greater today. Psychologists, behavioral scientists, and ethologists are more than ever interested in animal behavior as it occurs in the field as well as in the laboratory, and "a dominant theme in the remarkable growth of interest in animal behavior during the past decade . . . has been the study of animal communicative systems . . ." (Alexander, 1964, p. 713). Not horse, dog, and pig so much now, perhaps, but insect and octopus, gorilla and rhesus, dolphin and mynah bird are objects of intensive study. The layman, too, shares in the increased interest in animal behavior through the publication of books that are at once scholarly and popular (for example, Broadhurst, 1963). Broadhurst mentions the case of Clever Hans as illustrating Lloyd Morgan's canon—the principle that we should infer in animals only the lowest level of mental ability that is consistent with their observed behavior.

Angell believed that Pfungst's work was also relevant to the interest then invested in "telepathy" and "muscle reading." Only a few years after Pfungst's investigation of Clever Hans's ability, the American psychologist Stratton (1921), who had been a student of Wundt's, undertook a similar investigation of a famous muscle reader of the time.[6] Eugen de Rubini was able to read the "thoughts" of others by reading their patterns of muscle tension. All the mystery and excitement surrounding the horse of Mr. von Osten emerged for de Rubini's amazing abilities. And as Hans had his Pfungst to make his case one of scientific importance, so did de Rubini have his Stratton. Stratton's investigation was similar in strategy to that of Pfungst. The psychologist E. C. Tolman was present throughout all the experiments, and another psychologist, Warner Brown, was present during most of them.[7] The subject, de Rubini, held one end of a watch chain and his guide held the other end. The guide was to think of some object in the room that would then be identified by de Rubini. Success, which occurred much more often than it should by chance, was the more remarkable because the watch chain's slackness would seem to reduce the likelihood of muscle tension being transmitted. Although de Rubini was a professional performer he made no claims of supernatural power and was quite willing to be tested under controlled conditions after the manner of Mr. von Osten. And, as in the case of Clever Hans, no observer was able to detect a gross sensory cue to de Rubini. As a matter of fact, de Rubini's performace tended to worsen if a guide intentionally tried to help him by giving him gross cues. When the muscle reader held the end of the slack watch chain his success rate was twice as high as would be predicted on the basis of chance alone. When he did not hold the watch chain his success rate dropped to about one and one-half times as compared with what might occur by chance. When auditory cues to the subject were reduced his performance actually increased, a fact suggesting that some background sounds interfered with his performance. To achieve maximal accuracy, de Rubini required only peripheral visual contact with his questioner-guide. Total elimination of visual cues reduced his successes to about the level of chance, but the nature of his errors was not random. He was closer to naming the right object more often than could be expected if he were obtaining no information at all from his guide. Clear failure of de Rubini's abilities occurred only when both visual and auditory cues were drastically reduced. Thus we can see that Pfungst's strategy for investigating the case of Clever Hans was largely taken over by Stratton and his colleagues, Tolman and Brown, in their investigation of de Rubini. Unlike Pfungst, however, these investigators never did identify the precise cues employed by their subject.

Two years after Stratton's study of the muscle reader, W. S. Foster (1923) undertook a strategically similar series of experiments to investigate the role of unintentional communication in the ability to divine the presence of water and metals. Just as Stratton had been assisted by Tolman and Brown, so was Foster assisted by two eminent psychologists, R. M. Elliott and D. G. Paterson.

The subject of their study was a 70-year-old pastor of a church located in a small town near the University of Minnesota. He had a 45-year history of successfully locating not only water, gold, and silver but oil, natural gas, and iron as well. His feats had been observed by respectable and tough-minded critics, including professional engineers. That there was nothing fraudulent about his performance had been inferred from his vocation and from the fact that he requested the Psychological Laboratories at the University of Minnesota to study his rod-divining powers scientifically. He shared with von Osten and de Rubini a willingness to be "exposed" if that were to be the verdict of the scientists.

One of the experiments undertaken in order to stimulate field conditions required the subject to locate the course of water mains leading to two buildings on the campus. The rod diviner was accompanied by an experimenter who knew the location of the water mains in question. The results of this study suggested that the subject was not only able to locate the path of the water mains more accurately than could reasonably be attributed to chance but that he could also gauge the depth of the pipes. Foster's interpretation of this result was that quite without intention the old man was able to read subtle cues unintentionally emitted by the accompanying experimenter.

For another experiment a small cardboard box was filled with silver coins and silver and gold watches. The task in this experiment was for the subject to divine the depth of these materials. The pastor stood in a second floor hallway holding a 20-inch wire divining rod. In the first-floor hallway, immediately beneath the pastor, a 13-rung ladder was placed. By varying the rungs on which the materials to be located were placed, the depth of the metals relative to the subject could be varied at random. On a landing between the first and second floors a group of observers was placed in such a way that they could see both the ladder on the first floor and the rod diviner on the second floor. In spite of the fact that the spectators had been cautioned to avoid emitting cues to the subject, and in spite of the subject's sincere inattention to the spectators, he was able to gauge the depth of the metals far better than chance would allow. In fact, the correlation between the actual and the divined depth was found to be +.77 for a series of 26 trials. It seemed likely that the unintended and involuntary movements by the spectators served the necessary cueing function in this series of trials. Another possible source of cues to the subject in this study was a faintly audible sound from the first-floor hallway associated with the experimenter's placing and replacing materials on the various rungs of the ladder. These sounds were, however, probably even less audible when masked by the slight noise associated with the group of spectators.

When the same task was set for the rod diviner *without* any observers present who knew the correct answer the subject's performance fell off dramatically, although it did not seem to disappear. The correlation between the actual and divined depth fell from the previous $+.77$ to $+.29$. This somewhat better-than-chance accuracy seemed best interpreted as due to the subject's hearing the faint noise of the experimenter below climbing up and down the ladder.

As a more definitive test of the rod diviner's accuracy the following experiment was carried out. On a large and sturdy table 14 squares were marked off in alignment with 14 squares on the floor below. Cardboard screens shielded the squares under the table from observation. An experimenter placed the box of coins and watches in one of the randomly selected squares beneath the table and then left the room. Each square was selected twice for a total of 28 trials. The experimenter who recorded the subject's divinations did not know the location of the hidden materials. Under these conditions the pastor, standing on the table, was totally unable to locate the coins and watches. As in the case of Clever Hans, when no one was about who knew the correct answer and could unintentionally clue the subject, performance fell to a chance level.

When Foster instituted another table-top experiment in which the amount of material was varied, and in which the experimenter who knew the correct amount was present, performance again began to improve to a nearly significantly better-than-chance level. In this series of trials the experimenter said only the word "ready" to the subject, after having varied the amount of material in the cardboard box. Foster felt that the tone in which this single word was uttered might have unintentionally communicated some information about the right answer to the subject.

Involuntary cueing of subjects in experiments in extra-sensory perception (ESP) has long been discussed. In 1898, Moll repeated Alexander Wernicke's still earlier warning that muscle tremors on the part of the sender might influence the response of the receiver. Some 40 years after this and similar warnings had been sounded Kennedy (1938, 1939), in an improved replication of a much earlier experiment (Hansen and Lehmann, 1895), was able to show by the use of parabolic sound reflectors that senders in experiments on telepathy could unconsciously whisper or otherwise signal by auditory cues the right answers to the receivers. All this occurs, of course, not only in complete innocence after the manner of Mr. von Osten but also of Pfungst, Stumpf, Stratton, Tolman, Brown, Foster, Elliott, and Paterson. The subtlety of cues sufficient to inform subjects of the correct response was amply demonstrated by J. G. Miller (1942), who showed that subjects could perceive subtle cues at levels of illumination ordinarily found to be subthreshold.

Angell's comment in his Preface to this volume that Pfungst's findings would have relevance to an understanding of ESP and muscle reading was not only accurate but also, as it proved, prophetic.

"Talking" and "reading" horses, dogs, and pigs; clairvoy-ants, muscle readers, and rod diviners—the very mention of these oddities is enough to make the blood boil in the veins of some of the tough-minded psychologists of today. The phe-nomena are still too imperfectly analyzed to receive impor-tant consideration in the modern course in introductory psychology. Nevertheless, these topics have engaged some of the best minds of the day, and sophisticated research techniques were employed by these men to study their phenomena. The classical conditioning of Pavlov seems a more solid field; it was Pavlov who noted the unintentional communication process between laboratory experimenter and laboratory animal (Razran, 1959; Zirkle, 1958). Pavlov had been interested in the Lamarckian problem of the inheritance of acquired characteristics and had conducted some research in this area. It seemed that successive generations of trained mice were better able to learn, but at the Thirteenth International Physiological Congress held in Boston in August, 1929, Pavlov offered a fascinating postscript to his puzzling data. He reported that a closer check of his data suggested that there was no such increased learning ability on the part of the mice; instead there was an increased teaching ability on the part of his research assistant (Gruenberg, 1929). Unfortunately, from this interesting information alone we are in no position to state just how the experimenter unintentionally instructed his mouse subjects.

There was also the important work of H. M. Johnson (1913) on auditory discrimination and learning in dogs.[8] He presented an extended critique of Kalischer's earlier work, which indicated that his dogs could correctly anticipate the experimenter's next response from his posture, respiration, and the pattern of strain and relaxation of the muscles of the head and body. These cues too were obviously of an unintended and involuntary nature, as had been the case with Hans's questioners. And, as in their case, the experimenter's expectations were likely to be the antecedent conditions of an unintended communication process. Johnson also cited the work of Max Rothmann, who, as early as 1908, only one year after the appearance of Pfungst's work with Clever Hans, believed Kalischer's dogs to have reacted in the same manner as Hans. As a control for the Clever Hans phenomenon, Rothmann employed as an experimenter a servant who was unaware of the purpose of the investigation. That even under these conditions dogs could profit from the experimenter's unintended cues did not surprise Johnson. Dogs could, after all, learn a servant's signaling system as easily as a psychologist's. Johnson himself introduced the necessary controls into this situation by using a series of experiments in which the dogs could not see him at all, presumably eliminating visual cues effectively. To partially control auditory cues Johnson suggested that the experimenter not watch the dogs' responses. Thus the behavior of the dogs could not elicit a change in the vocal behavior of the investigator, whose expectations might have led to changes in his respiration as a result of his observation of the dogs' responses. When all the proper controls had been instituted, Johnson found that no discrimination abilities at all could be demonstrated for the dogs.

That minimal cues, unintentionally emitted by the experimenter, might influence the subject's response has also been suggested for psychophysical experiments. In an experiment on the judgment of weights, Warner and Raible (1937) removed the experimenter from the visual field of the subject. In half the trials the experimenter knew which answer was correct, and in half he was kept uninformed. Only 6 of the 17 subjects showed a large discrepancy from a chance distribution of errors, but all of the 6 subjects made more errors on those trials in which the experimenter did not know the correct answers himself. The authors suggested that some form of auditory cue might have been emitted by the experimenter. That this cue was not likely to be vocal was suggested by the fact that the experimenter kept his mouth tightly closed in order to prevent unconscious whispering or any other unintended vocal signaling. These investigations, like most of the others just discussed, did not succeed in isolating (as Pfungst had been able to do) the specific cues employed.

A paradigm similar to that used by Warner and Raible, and one very much in the tradition of Clever Hans, was chosen by Stanton and Baker (1942). In a study of the retention of geometric figures 200 undergraduate students were tested by five experienced workers. These experimenters had with them a key of the "correct" responses, some of which were intentionally listed incorrectly. Experimenters were explicitly cautioned to avoid any biasing effect of the knowledge of the "correct" responses. Nevertheless, results of the retention test showed that, when the incorrect answer had been substituted for the correct one on the experimenter's key, his subjects were more often "correctly" incorrect in their response. By some cue or other, experimenters must have communicated their expectation to their subjects. In spite of the fact that Lindzey (1951) and Friedman (1942) were unable to replicate these findings, the results were so striking and so consistent with some of the earlier findings described here that it seems improper to dismiss them. In fact Stanton (1942a) later presented additional evidence to strengthen his conclusion. Again employing nonsense materials, he had three groups of experimenters test subjects for retention. One group of experimenters knew which of the materials had been shown to subjects earlier. Another group of experimenters was intentionally misinformed as to which materials had been shown to subjects, and a third group was told nothing. Results of this experiment also indicated that experimenters had in some way communicated their knowledge of the correct answers to their subjects—subtly and unintentionally.

A final example of the unintentional cueing of subjects is the case briefly reported by Wilson (1952). The experimental task required an apparently difficult discrimination between the presence and absence of a faint light. Ability to discriminate appeared to depend in part on the experimenter's recording system. It turned out that maximal discrimination occurred when the experimenter, using a scratchy pen, unintentionally cued the subject by a short pen scratch for no light and a long pen scratch for the light.

It is interesting to compare the results of the investigations described with the results of Pfungst's experiments. All these investigators learned something about the experimenters' unintentional communication with their subjects. But with the possible exception of the case described by Wilson (1952)—which seems to have been a much simpler one than any of the others—no one but Pfungst succeeded in specifying the exact cues that had been unwittingly emitted to the subject. Johnson had been able to implicate the experimenter's respiratory pattern, but he could not be sure of it. Stratton, Foster, and Warner and Raible were able to state only the sense modalities likely to be involved in the unintended communication. Pavlov, and Stanton and Baker, could not specify the modalities involved at all. Of all the complicated cases of unintentional communication studied, only Pfungst's case can be regarded as having been completely solved. Taking all the cases together does suggest, however, that ordinary, though often extremely subtle, sensory cues may be sufficient to explain the unwitting communication between experimenters and subjects. Some more recent attempts, both to elicit and to elucidate such unwitting communication, will be described in the following section.

III

In many of the cases of the Clever Hans phenomenon the subtle and unintentional cueing of the subject by the experimenter could be attributed to the experimenter's expectancy. Pfungst, for example, considered expectation and its attendant tension as helping him to account for the communication of correct responses to Clever Hans (see p. 147).

In general Hans performed accurately only for those questioners who consciously or unconsciously believed he could. Merton's (1948) concept of the self-fulfilling prophecy seems relevant: one behaves in such a way as to increase the likelihood of the prophesied event. That many experimenters over the years may have fulfilled their experimental prophecies by unintentionally communicating information to their subjects may be a disquieting proposition. We will probably never know what proportion of behavioral researches have been affected by the unintended communication of experimenter expectancies. This problem, the Clever Hans phenomenon, has occupied the present writer's attention for most of the last decade.

With horses so hard to come by and troublesome as laboratory animals, rats will do. A dozen students of experimental psychology served as experimenters in a study of the learning of a brightness discrimination in which rats were purported to have been specially bred for cleverness (Rosenthal and Fode, 1963). Each experimenter trained five animals a day for five days. Half the experimenters were told that their animals were from the "Berkeley Colony: Maze Bright Division," and the remaining experimenters were told that their animals were from the "Maze Dull Division." The experimenters' expectations were thus manipulated by alleged reference to the subjects' genetic history. All the rats were, of course, from a homogeneous population and were assigned at random to experimenters. At the end of the first day's running, the animals used by experimenters expecting better performance outperformed the animals used by experimenters expecting poorer performance. The difference found was statistically significant and held up over the full five-day schedule. Animals believed to be bright made half again as many correct responses as those believed to be dull. The particular discrimination employed was a difficult one, and the animals often refused to make any response at all. Moreover, among animals used by experimenters expecting good performance no running at all occurred on 11% of the trials, whereas the animals used by experimenters expecting poor performance refused to run on 29% of the trials.

What cues could have been given the rats by their experimenters to account for the results of this experiment? It would be preposterous to suppose that the rats carefully observed the head movements of the experimenters as Hans had done, or listened for auditory cues as Johnson's dogs may have done. Still cues can operate, as it were, automatically. To this writer it seems more likely that these experimenters handled their rats differentially as a function of their expectancy about their abilities and that the differences in handling these animals led to the differences in their performance. How does one handle a rat believed to be bright? Perhaps more often and more gently; perhaps more "warmly" and enthusiastically than one handles an animal believed to be dull. Associated with the perception of animals' brightness in our sample of experimenters was the perception of animals' "character." Rats believed to be brighter were described by their experimenters as cleaner, tamer, and generally more pleasant. It may have been these associated characteristics that led the experimenters to handle their brighter-perceived animals differentially. In any case, experimenters who believed their subjects to be bright stated that they did handle these subjects more often and more gently than did the experimenters who expected less of their subjects.[9]

If, as Pfungst and others found, the expectancies of experimenters are communicated so readily to their animal subjects, we might expect that they can also be communicated to their human subjects. For this reason a series of studies was undertaken to learn the role of the experimenters' expectancy in influencing the responses of their human subjects. A task of person-perception was employed in many of these investigations (Rosenthal, 1963). Subjects were asked to judge what degree of success had been experienced by each person pictured in a series of photographs. The subjects rated each photo from very unsuccessful (-10) to mildly unsuccessful (-1) to mildly successful ($+1$) to very successful ($+10$). The photos, cut from a magazine, had been standardized to evoke average ratings of zero (neither successful nor unsuccessful). The basic procedure employed in many of these studies was to draw a random sample of experimenters and to lead half of them to expect that the subjects assigned to them would tend to see the people pictured as failures. The remaining experimenters were led to expect that their subjects would tend to see the people pictured as successes. Actually, of course, subjects were simply assigned to their experimenters at random. All experimenters were given identical instructions to read to their subjects. Nevertheless, in three studies in which 30 experimenters each used about a dozen subjects, the lowest average rating obtained by any experimenter expecting high ratings was higher than the highest average rating obtained by any experimenter expecting low ratings from his subjects. In all three studies these nonoverlapping distributions of experimental results differed very significantly from any results that could be attributed to chance.

The conclusion to be drawn from these and subsequent studies (Rosenthal, 1964) is that in some subtle, unintentional way experimenters do communicate their expectations to their human subjects, whose performance is then significantly altered. There remains, however, the most urgent question: How do the experimenters communicate to their subjects what it is they expect of them?

The exquisite sensitivity of human subjects to these "demand characteristics" has been amply documented by Martin Orne (1962). Data from several experiments, including a careful analysis of sound motion pictures of interactions between the experimenter and his subject, suggest that no gross procedural errors are responsible; neither words nor readily perceptible gestures carry the burden of communication. The explanation does not lie in the infrequent occurrence of biased errors of observation, recording, and computation.

Now it seems reasonable to suppose that the cues employed by experimenters who intentionally tried to influence their subjects might appear as simple exaggerations of more subtle cues employed when the experimenters were influencing their subjects unintentionally. Accordingly, sound motion picture films were made of three experimenter-subject interactions in which the photo-rating task was employed. Each experimenter was assigned at random a number between —10 and +10. It was made the experimenter's task to influence his subject to rate the stimulus photos as close to the randomly assigned numerical value as possible. The three films were then viewed by a large group of observers who, of course, were not told what rating each experimenter was trying to elicit from his subject. All observers made an effort to guess the numerical value each of the three experimenters was trying to obtain from his subject. These guesses proved to be so accurate there can be little doubt that the observers accurately "read" an experimenter's expectancy when he intentionally tried to influence his subject's responses.[10]

When observers can agree so well on an experimenter's expectancy, we would expect them also to agree on the channel of communication involved. Numerous hypotheses were suggested by the observers, but there were few agreements on the specific cues employed. There appeared, however, to be two promising dimensions for the location of hypotheses. One of these had to do with timing; that is, when in the social interaction the communication occurred. The other had to do with sense modality; that is, whether the cues were more visual-kinesic or more auditory-paralinguistic.[11] For many observers the communication of expectancy was judged to occur only after the subject began making his responses. These observers were our "reinforcement theorists," who pointed out that when subjects gave a response close to the desired value, the experimenter responded with positive reinforcing cues such as smiling, head-nodding, looking more pleased or interested, and recording the responses more vigorously. The reinforcement theorists pointed out, moreover, that when subjects gave responses not in accordance with the expectancy, the experimenters employed negative reinforcing cues—head-shaking, eyebrow-raising, looking surprised or disappointed, repeating the response aloud, tapping the pencil, holding the stimulus photo up longer, tilting the photo forward, and "throwing" the photo down on the table. There was good agreement among observers that no two experimenters showed exactly the same pattern of reinforcements.

Opposed to the reinforcement theorists were observers who felt that communication of expectancy preceded subjects' response to the experimental task. These theorists were divided as to the nature of the cues involved. One type, the specifist, emphasized the potential cues associated with the experimenter's reading of the instructions to the subject. These observers believed they had noted a greater emphasis on the desired alternative when the subject's alternative responses were described for him by the experimenter, but there was little agreement on the form of this emphasis. Vocal stress in speech was suggested as one form of emphasis, but so were stammering, changing the rate of speech, making more reading errors, and pointing a little longer at that region of the rating scale from which the subject was to select his response.

The other type of nonreinforcement theorist was the generalist, who tended to de-emphasize the importance of any single, small cues. Instead these observers emphasized the general climate created by the experimenter from the very beginning of his interaction with his subject. Thus, the experimenters who expected more positive ratings from their subjects were seen as creating a more positive tone, whereas those who expected negative ratings were seen as creating a more negative tone. As part of this general tone the experimenters' ocular dynamics were specifically noted: greater eye-contact was associated with positive tone and visual-avoidance with negative tone.

The great differences in what the observers saw on looking at the intentional communication of the experimenter's expectancy are reminiscent of the early search for the key to communication of information to Clever Hans. In this case, however, the analysis is not as yet at hand—neither for intentional nor for unintentional communication.

In his Introduction to the present volume Stumpf confessed that he had expected to find auditory cues for Hans rather than minute visual cues—cues so subtle that even expert observers who expected them could not detect them. Still Stumpf was not altogether wrong, for in at least some tasks it appeared that auditory cues were of some value to Hans. When Hans was asked to fetch placards with certain words written upon them or to select one of several colored cloths, Mr. von Osten would shout at him if he approached the wrong stimulus—thereby directing him to the correct one. In experimental observation of this task Pfungst found Hans to be about 30% accurate with benefit of visual cues alone. When auditory cues were added, Hans's performance jumped to over 50% accuracy.

Following closely in Pfungst's footsteps, Fode (1960) undertook a study directed at learning the relative contribution of visual and auditory cues to the process by which an experimenter unintentionally communicates his expectancy to his subjects. The standard photo-rating task was administered by 24 experimenters to 180 men and women subjects. The 24 experimenters were randomly assigned to one of four groups. One group of six experimenters, the *control* group, was led to expect their subjects to rate the photos as being of unsuccessful people. The remaining three experimental groups of six experimenters each were led to expect their subjects to rate the photos as being of successful people. The experimental groups differed from each other in the types of cues they unwittingly sent their subjects. The experimenters permitting *visual cues* were visible to their subjects, but remained entirely silent except for greeting their subjects and handing them written instructions. The experimenters permitting *auditory cues* read their instructions to subjects aloud, but were hidden from their subjects' view by an interposed screen. Those free to give both *visual and auditory cues* read their instructions to their subjects and also remained in full view. This group differed from the control group only in the induced expectancy.

The results of this study showed no difference in obtained photo-ratings between the group permitted visual cues and the control group, a result which suggested, among other interpretations, that visual cues alone were insufficient to carry the burden of the unintended communication or that the strangeness to the subjects of an apparently unnecessarily aloof and mute experimenter led to their rating the photos as more unsuccessful. The group permitted auditory cues obtained significantly more ratings of success than did the control group, a result suggesting that auditory-paralinguistic cues alone might be sufficient to communicate experimenters' expectancies to subjects. The group permitted both visual and auditory cues obtained significantly more ratings of success than did the group permitted only auditory cues. It appeared, then, that the effects of auditory cues, although sufficient, could be significantly increased (approximately "doubled") by the addition of visual cues, even though the effect of visual cues alone was at best only equivocal. In any case, it seems clear that neither the strategy nor the tactics of inquiry employed by Pfungst are in any way outmoded or irrelevant to contemporary psychology.

Pfungst had noted among questioners of Hans that some were more successful than others in having their expectancies confirmed by Hans's responses. The configuration of the characteristics that Pfungst observed to be associated with more successful unintentional influencers of Hans is very like that observed to be associated with more successful unintentional influencers of human subjects. Thus Pfungst discovered that an air of authority about the questioner increased the likelihood of his influencing Hans, and now current experiments show that an air of authority increases the effects of experimenters' expectancies upon their human subjects. Pfungst found that ability and tact in dealing with animals led to more expected responses from Hans. The current experiments show that an interpersonal style, reflecting a relaxed, personal, interested, and involved approach to human subjects, also tends to maximize the effects of an experimenter's expectancy. Pfungst found that experimenters who were more gesturally inclined were more able to influence Hans's responses. Similarly it now appears that experimenters more inclined to gesture are unintentionally more influential in determining their human subjects' responses.

Pfungst also noted even Hans's better questioners became more successful in eliciting the expected responses as they had more practice. A similar learning-effect has been observed in these studies of the experimenter's expectancy as it affects human subjects. For these, as for Hans's experimenters, their subjects' responding in accordance with their expectancy may well have served as reinforcement. Whatever small, unintended visual or auditory cues were produced by the experimenters would have then become more likely to recur when they increased the likelihood of obtaining an expected response. Pfungst's findings, as well as the present ones, may be interpreted to mean that not only does the experimenter unknowingly evoke expected responses from his subject but that the subject also unwittingly evokes appropriate cues from his experimenter.

Pfungst and Stumpf summarized their difficulties in learning the nature of Clever Hans's talents by speaking of "looking for, in the horse, what should have been sought in the man." There may be many other areas of contemporary psychological inquiry in which what we have looked for in our *subjects* should have been sought in ourselves as *experimenters*.

IV

Are there methodological morals to be drawn from the case of Clever Hans? Whatever questions we may have to put to horse or man might best be asked by any collector of data who has no specific expectancy regarding what the answer ought to be. The ultimate collector of data, were we to insist on an absence of any expectation regarding subjects' responses, would have to be some sort of machine. Nor is this such a bizarre notion, for there exist now automated systems for the collection of data that drastically reduce—though they do not quite eliminate—contact between experimenter and subject. Someone must still place the animal into the automatic apparatus.

Considering that in much contemporary behavioral research experimenters have contact with at least two types of subjects, some from an "experimental" and others from a "control" group, the experimenter's knowledge of the subject's group membership is likely to affect his expectancy regarding their responses. In order that their expectancies should not affect the two kinds of subjects differentially, some investigators have taken to recording their instructions to subjects on tape so as to assure standard presentation to subjects under different experimental conditions. That would seem to be a reasonable safeguard against the experimenter's tone of voice (and other paralinguistic features) influencing his subjects' responses differentially. We can well imagine that, if Pfungst had had tape recorders available, he would have recorded his questions for Hans, started the tape by remote control, simultaneously activating a motion picture camera directed at Hans's trained foot. If Hans had tapped at all, he would of course still be tapping with no visual cues to stop him. But he might not have tapped, and Mr. von Osten would then have complained that Hans's training had not included any audio-visual instruction and that to be realistic a human questioner must be employed—and Mr. von Osten would have been exactly right. Nor is this fantasy entirely irrelevant to contemporary psychological research. There are experiments waiting to be conducted, many of them in social psychology, which would simply make no sense at all without a present and fully operating human experimenter. In these cases it is still possible to assess the relative contribution to subjects' responses of the experimenter's expectancy even though it cannot be eliminated.

This result could be accomplished by the frequent employment of "expectancy control groups," and there are very few areas of behavioral research which would not benefit from such a technique. Pfungst utilized such expectancy controls when he employed some experimenters who, because they knew the right answer to the question put to Hans, expected him to stop tapping at a certain number, and other experimenters who had no such expectancy. We can generalize this procedure in the light of what we know both about the effects of the experimenter's expectancy and current methods of research.

Consider any experiment in which two different conditions are involved: one regarded as an experimental and the other as a control condition. Examples are a new teaching method vs. an old one; a new drug vs. a placebo; two types of psychotherapy; a salient and a nonsalient persuasive communication. The experiment is being conducted, in the first place, because we think one of these conditions will lead subjects to respond differently from the other. The subjects in one group will learn faster or lose their symptoms sooner or change their personalities more or alter their attitudes more. If we are concerned, as we should be, about the effects of expectancies on subjects' responses, we can introduce another experimental dimension in which we vary the expectancy of the data collector. Without necessarily increasing the total number of subjects involved we would merely divide the experiment into two halves. One half of the subjects in the "experimental" condition would be interviewed by data collectors who had been led to expect that the theoretical effect (change or improvement or difference) would occur. The other half of the subjects, though receiving the same programmed treatment (drug, communication, and so on) would, however, be seen by experimenters led to believe that there would be no effect—perhaps by a false labeling of the group or by disparagement of the effectiveness of the treatment. Similarly, among the subjects of the "control" condition, half would be interviewed by experimenters who expected the effect of the experimental manipulation and half would be seen by experimenters who expected no effect. Appropriate statistical analysis of the results of such an expectancy-controlled experiment would permit an assessment of the magnitude of the effects of the experimental variables of primary interest in relation to the effects of the experimenter's expectancy.[12]

Appropriate to the discussion of methodological issues, but important in its own right, is Pfungst's interest in the various sense modalities by which man may communicate with animals. If we knew precisely by what means we unintentionally communicate our expectancies to our animal and human subjects, we could institute more effective controls against the effect of our expectancies. More generally, if we knew more about the modalities by which we subtly and unintentionally influence one another, we would then have learned a great deal that is new about human social behavior. Pfungst emphasized the visual and auditory sense modalities in his study of Clever Hans. Subsequent investigators have also tended to emphasize the role of these modalities in interpersonal influence. At present there appears in fact to be a renaissance of interest in the role of kinesic and paralinguistic information as it contributes to the total process of communication (Sebeok, Hayes, & Bateson, 1964).

Not so much in connection with Hans as with respect to horse and rider relations generally, Pfungst discussed the importance of kinesthetic and tactual cues. By means of these cues horses are virtually able to anticipate the wishes of the rider quite without the rider's awareness. The role of the skin senses in human communication has recently been brought into focus by Geldard (1960), who has presented evidence for a remarkable sensitivity of the skin even to human speech. For some time it was supposed that the blind were enabled to avoid obstacles through an exquisite sensitivity of the skin of the face, called "facial vision," but it has been shown that the sense modality actually involved is auditory. Recent ingenious studies carried out by Kellogg (1962) suggest that the blind at least may employ a technique of echo ranging (sonar) to obtain information about their environment, much in the manner of the bat and the porpoise. Kellogg's human subjects were able to assess accurately the distance, size, and composition of objects in their environment.

One very neglected modality from the viewpoint of interpersonal communication is the olfactory. Vision and audition are useful in human communication, not only because these senses convey so much information about the environment, including the people in it, but also because these senses tell us much about even small changes in the interpersonal environment. Olfaction may or may not be capable of giving human beings this sort of information. Although little empirical research has been conducted on this question, it seems reasonable to assert that, because we are alert to such small changes in others' facial expressions and tones of voice, we could be sensitive to changes in odors of others.[13] A great deal of research would seem to be needed here. When we know much more than we do now about communication by minimal cues of any sense modality, we will be in a far better position to understand the structure and dynamics of such interpersonal relationships as those that occur in families, schools, businesses, clinics and hospitals—and in the collecting of data too.

NOTES

1. The book which lies ahead is Pfungst's, yet in noting that Stumpf was both a collaborator of Pfungst and eminent as well, more should be said about him. What could and should be said has been said by Boring (1950). One of the most important (but clearly not *the* most important) of the German psychologists of the waning years of the last century, Stumpf nevertheless held the most important chair of psychology in all Germany, the one at the University of Berlin. Oskar Pfungst was one of his outstanding students. That Pfungst should have conducted the investigation of Clever Hans at Stumpf's suggestion made sense, for Stumpf often turned experimental enterprises over to students who would accept them. As Boring (1950) put it: "Stumpf was an experimentalist by philosophical conviction but not by temperament" (p. 371).

Stumpf, of course, was one of the thirteen courageous men who risked their professional reputations by absolving Hans from the reception of any observed cues, and Albert Moll in an acrimonious context (1910), refers to the "September Report" of 1904 as that "deplorable report," for he claimed to have known all along, on the basis of his own study of Hans, what was really going on. Poor Stumpf was berated for not having known, as Moll thought any worker in the area of hypnosis would, that small cues can be effective communicating agents even when unobserved by the sender or bystanders. Moll further implied that the research program carried out by Pfungst owed much of its technique to Moll's experiments with Hans, experiments which he said had already been reported to the Psychological Society of Berlin. Ultimately Moll called Stumpf a liar (p. 458), but Stumpf survived the attack (by some 30 years, in fact) and even got in some thrusts of his own, as can be seen in some of Stumpf's supplementary sections included in this book. (When reading these sections such phrases as "obscure irresponsibles" are best read as "Albert Moll".) H. M. Johnson (1911) was right when he remarked that the name-calling aspects of the controversy did "scant credit to either of the parties" (p. 666).

Less fortunate in the matter of survival was Mr. von Osten, nor is it here quite so easy to view the controversy as somewhat quaint. Mr. von Osten, unlike scientific antagonists, had everything to lose and nothing comparable to gain by having his

Hans investigated. He must indeed have been completely honest and sincere and the findings in this book grieved him deeply, nor could he accept them. Within a few months he died. (Johnson, 1911).

2. Of Pfungst's work H. M. Johnson (1911) said: "His account may be read with the interest of an exciting novel, and yet with great and lasting profit by anyone at all interested in animal behavior or in the problems of animal consciousness, whether his interest be that of the comparative psychologist, the naturalist, or the mere lover of domestic animals" (see page 633).

3. The teacher of psychology can nicely employ Pfungst's inquiry as an illustration of John Stuart Mill's major principles of scientific method as set forth in his *Logic* of 1843. Mill's method of agreement, the observation of systematic consequences of an event, is illustrated by Pfungst's observation that Hans's cleverness followed his viewing a questioner who knew the answer to the question posed. Mill's method of difference, the more powerful principle, requires not only systematic consequences of an event but also the *absence* of these consequences in the *absence* of the event. This principle is illustrated by Pfungst's employment of blinders and of questioners who did not know the answers to their questions. Mill's method of concomittant variations, an extension of the method of difference, requires that changes in the magnitude of the consequences are systematically related to changes in the magnitude of the antecedent. This principle is illustrated by Pfungst's observation of the relationship between the questioner's distance from Hans and Hans's cleverness. (See also the discussion of Mill's methods by Boring [1954].)

4. All these clever animals were of interest to Pfungst and are cited by him in the present volume except the last, a much more recent case. Lady, the talking horse of Richmond, Virginia, was in some ways very much like Hans, only more "ambitious." She could not only count and spell but she could also locate missing objects, foretell the future, and even venture to give personal and financial advice. It was said that a friend of Lady's owner consulted Lady before making any important decisions. Like Hans, Lady attracted considerable attention, but, unlike Hans's owner, Lady's owner, a Mrs. Claudia Fonda, charged a nominal fee for her horse's services.

Whatever Lady's talents were, she had a more sophisticated method of replying to questions than Hans. Where Hans could only tap or not tap, Lady had learned to operate a special typewriter. With her nose she would flip up letters and numbers in sequence to form her brief replies. (Pictures of Lady employing her apparatus can be found in *Life* magazine of December 22, 1952, Vol. 33, No. 25.)

A thoroughly dependable informant, a research worker in another discipline (who, because of his modesty, prefers that I do not use his name), not only made me aware of the Virginia horse but observed her skill at firsthand. He and his wife owned a prize dog which had recently disappeared. The Virginia horse, reputed to be a good finder of lost objects, was consulted. My friend's wife, convinced that the dog had come to some harm, inquired of his whereabouts. The horse spelled out the word "dead." A few days later the pet turned up very much alive. My friend's interpretation, with which it is easy to agree, was that the owner of the horse sensed the questioner's conviction that the dog was dead. In some way, not at all apparent to even a keen observer, the horse's owner must have communicated to her the sequence of appropriate keyboard responses. It is one thing to find the cues that start and stop a horse's tapping. It is quite another to find the cues that lead a horse to choose one letter out of 26 and then another and another, especially when the "keys" of the typewriter are quite close together. To learn the unintentional (if it was unintentional) signaling system in this case would have provided Pfungst with another worthy challenge.

5. Pfungst's encounter with Hans was not to be his last investigation of a clever animal. Only a few years later he was to study the conversational ability of "Don," a seven-year-old German setter. Don's "von Osten" was not an academic but a royal game warden by the name of Ebers. Don did not bark, tap, or type his answers, but rather spoke them—or so it was said. Don could "pronounce" his name, the nouns "hunger," "cake," "rest," and the verb "to have." Like Hans, Don could be asked questions in any language, though each was confined to one language in responding (taps in one case, German in the other). Pfungst showed his thoroughness once again in his investigation of Don, this time making phonographic recordings of Don's "speech." The case of Don was simpler than the case of Hans. It turned out that people simply heard him say what they expected and wanted him to say. From the phonographic recordings it became clear that if Don could speak, then he suffered from a disorder of articulation. More important, it was quickly established

that Don answered all questions with answers learned in sequence. If the questions were asked in the right order, the answers, though poorly articulated, would be approximately correct. If the question order was varied, the answers were wrong. All in all, Don did not represent the same degree of challenge to Pfungst that Hans had offered or that the talking horse of Richmond might have provided if Pfungst had been there to look into it. Some additional details of the case of Don are to be found in H. M. Johnson's report (1912).

6. Let me thank Marvin Hoffman for calling this work to my attention.

7. This was a brilliant trio of investigators, all three from the University of California at Berkeley. In accordance with the criterion of multiple mention by Boring (1948, 1950), all were major figures in the history of psychology. Compare this illustrious group to Pfungst, who, though he is mentioned in passing by Boring (1950), has been virtually unknown by American psychologists. Pfungst did indeed enjoy local fame, not only through his work with Hans but also through his writing for the popular press.

8. Let me thank E. G. Boring for calling this and other work by Johnson (and the early work of J. G. Miller) to my attention.

9. A second experiment was conducted to check on the results of this first one and to extend the generality of its findings (Rosenthal and Lawson, 1964). The learning tasks for the animals were posed within the context of Skinner boxes; half the experimenters were told that their animals were "Skinner-box dull," while the remainder were told that their animals were "Skinner-box bright." Subjects were again labeled bright and dull at random and assigned to the research groups at random. This was a more longitudinal experiment in that experimenters worked with the same animals over the course of an entire academic quarter. Seven specific experiments were performed: magazine training, operant acquisition, extinction and spontaneous recovery, secondary reinforcement, stimulus discrimination, stimulus generalization, and chaining of responses.

In this experiment, as in the earlier one, those experimenters who believed their animals were the better performers obtained significantly better performance than did the experimenters who believed their subjects to be the poorer performers. In this study, too, experimenters who believed their subjects to be brighter rated themselves as more pleasant vis-à-vis their animals and reported that they handled them more. Although less handling of subjects occurred generally in this Skinner-box study than in the maze-learning study, there was still opportunity for handling animals in transporting them from home cage to Skinner box and then back again at the end of the day's work. At the present time, and on the basis of the two studies described, we can conclude that experimenters' expectancy may be a significant determinant of their subjects' performance when those subjects are laboratory rats. Our best guess about the "cues" involved is that they are mediated to the subject by differential handling patterns. Visual and auditory cues have not been definitively ruled out for rat subjects, but they seem less likely to play the major role they have played in the experimenter-determined performances of horses, dogs, and pigs.

10. Altogether there were 52 observers, most of whom were graduate students. For each observer a rank-order correlation was computed between the number he guessed the experimenter was after and the number that actually had been assigned that experimenter. Where by chance we would expect 26 of these 52 correlations to be positive in sign, 48 were positive, and the median correlation was $+.88$. In a replication study involving five additional experimenter-subject dyads, a smaller group of 11 observers obtained a median correlation of $+.72$ between their guesses of the experimenters' expectancy and the expectancy actually assigned.

11. The terms "kinesics" and "paralinguistics" refer to two of the newer areas of study within the broader field of interpersonal communication. Kinesics is the study of those body movements that have relevance for the transmission of information (for example, gestures). Paralinguistics is the study of those vocal—but not specifically linguistic—behaviors that have similar relevance (for example, tone of voice). Both areas, subsumed under the more generic area of "semiotics," have come in for recent systematic attention (Sebeok, Hayes, & Bateson, 1964).

12. The employment of expectancy control groups, including details of the analysis of the results, has been discussed elsewhere (Rosenthal, 1964a).

13. Alexander Wernicke, the physicist-philosopher from Braunschweig, thought so—especially in the case of a hypnotist's subject whose "extremely delicate sense of smell" would be mobilized to try to "read" the hypnotist's expectation. A careful experimenter, Wernicke suggested that hypnotist and subject should be separated from one another by a glass partition (Moll, 1910, p. 518).

REFERENCES

Alexander, R. D. Communicative systems of animals: acoustic behavior. *Science,* 1964, 144, 713–715.

Boring, E. G. *A History of Experimental Psychology,* 2d ed. New York: Appleton-Century-Crofts, 1950.

Boring, E. G. The nature and history of experimental control. *Amer. J. Psychol.,* 1954, 67, 573–589.

Boring, E. G., and Mollie D. Boring. Masters and pupils among the American psychologists. *Amer. J. Psychol.,* 1948, 61, 527–534. Also reprinted in E. G. Boring, *History, Psychology, and Science: Selected Papers.* New York and London: Wiley, 1963, pp. 132–139.

Broadhurst, P. L. *The Science of Animal Behavior.* Baltimore, Md.: Penguin, 1963.

Brown, R. *Words and Things.* New York: Free Press of Glencoe, 1958.

Fode, K. L. The effect of non-visual and non-verbal interaction on experimenter bias. Unpublished master's thesis, University of North Dakota, 1960.

Foster, W. S. Experiments on rod-divining. *J. appl. Psychol.,* 1923, 7, 303–311.

Friedman, Pearl. A second experiment on interviewer bias. *Sociometry,* 1942, 5, 378–379.

Geldard, F. A. Some neglected possibilities of communication. *Science,* 1960, 131, 1583–1588.

Gruenberg, B. C. *The Story of Evolution.* Princeton, N.J.: Van Nostrand, 1929.

Hansen, F. C. C., and A. Lehmann. Ueber Unwillkürliches Flüstern. *Phil. Stud.,* 1895, 11, 471–530.

Johnson, H. M. Review of Pfungst, O., *Clever Hans* (New York: Holt, 1911). *J. Philos., Psychol. & Scientific Methods,* 1911, 8, 663–666.

Johnson, H. M. The talking dog. *Science,* 1912, 35, 749–751.

Johnson, H. M. Audition and habit formation in the dog. *Behav. Monogr.,* 1913, 2, no. 3, serial no. 8.

Kellogg, W. N. Sonar system of the blind. *Science,* 1962, 137, 399–404.

Kennedy, J. L. Experiments on "unconscious whispering." *Psychol. Bull.,* 1938, 35, 526. (Abstract)

Kennedy. J. L. A methodological review of extra-sensory perception. *Psychol. Bull.,* 1939, 36, 59–103.

Lindzey, G. A note on interviewer bias. *J. appl. Psychol.,* 1951, 35, 182–184.

Merton, R. K. The self-fulfilling prophecy. *Antioch Rev.,* 1948, 8, 193–210.

Mill, J. S. *A System of Logic, Ratiocinative and Inductive.* London: Longmans, 1925 (1843).

Miller, J. G. *Unconsciousness.* New York: Wiley, 1942.

Moll, A. *Hypnotism,* 4th ed. New York: Scribner's, 1898.

Moll, A. *Hypnotism,* 4th enlarged ed., trans. A. F. Hopkirk. New York: Scribner's, 1910; London: Walter Scott.

Orne, M. T. On the social psychology of the psychological experiment: with particular reference to demand characteristics and their implications. *Amer. Psychologist,* 1962, 17, 776–783.

Polanyi, M. *Personal Knowledge.* Chicago: University of Chicago Press, 1958.

Razran, G. Pavlov the empiricist. *Science,* 1959, 130, 916.

Rosenthal, R. The effect of the experimenter on the results of psychological research. In B. Maher, ed. *Progress in Experimental Personality Research.* Vol. I. New York: Academic Press, 1964.

Rosenthal, R. On the social psychology of the psychological experiment: the experimenter's hypothesis as unintended determinant of experimental results. *Amer. Scientist,* 1963, 51, 268–283.

Rosenthal, R. The control of experimenter expectancy effects. Unpublished manuscript, Harvard University, 1964a.

Rosenthal, R., and K. L. Fode. The effect of experimenter bias on the performance of the albino rat. *Behav. Sci.,* 1963, 8, 183–189.

Rosenthal, R., and R. Lawson. A longitudinal study of the effects of experimenter bias on the operant learning of laboratory rats. *J. Psychiat. Res.,* 1964, 2, 61–72.

Sebeok, T. A., A. S. Hayes, and Mary C. Bateson, eds. *Approaches to Semiotics.* The Hague: Mouton, 1964.

Stanton, F. Further contributions at the twentieth anniversary of the psychological corporation and to honor its founder, James McKeen Cattel. *J. appl. Psychol.,* 1942a, 26, 16–17.

Stanton, F., and K. H. Baker. Interviewer bias and the recall of incompletely learned materials. *Sociometry,* 1942, 5, 123–134.

Stratton, G. M. The control of another person by obscure signs *Psychol. Rev.*, 1921, 28, 310–314.

Warner, L., and Mildred Raible. Telepathy in the psychophysical laboratory. *J. Parapsychol.*, 1937, 1, 44–51.

Wilson, E. B. *An Introduction to Scientific Research.* New York: McGraw-Hill, 1952.

Zirkle, C. Pavlov's beliefs. *Science,* 1958, 128, 1476.

CLEVER HANS

(THE HORSE OF MR. VON OSTEN)

A CONTRIBUTION TO EXPERIMENTAL ANIMAL AND HUMAN PSYCHOLOGY

BY

OSKAR PFUNGST

WITH AN INTRODUCTION BY PROF. C. STUMPF,
AND ONE ILLUSTRATION AND FIFTEEN FIGURES

TRANSLATED FROM THE GERMAN
BY
CARL L. RAHN
Fellow in Psychology in the University of Chicago

WITH A PREFATORY NOTE BY
JAMES R. ANGELL
Professor of Psychology in the University of Chicago

NEW YORK
HENRY HOLT AND COMPANY
1911

PREFATORY NOTE

[By James R. Angell]

The University of Chicago

It gives me great pleasure to accept the invitation of the publishers to write a word of introduction for Mr. Rahn's excellent translation of "Der Kluge Hans", a book which in the original has been but little known to American readers. The present wave of interest in animal life and behavior renders its appearance peculiarly appropriate.

No more remarkable tale of credulity founded on unconscious deceit was ever told, and were it offered as fiction, it would take high rank as a work of imagination. Being in reality a record of sober fact, it verges on the miraculous. After reading Mr. Pfungst's story one can quite understand how sedate and sober Germany was for months thrown into a turmoil of newspaper debate, which for intensity and range of feeling finds its only parallel in a heated political campaign. That the subject of the controversy was the alleged ability of a trained horse to solve complex arithmetical problems may excite gaiety and even derision, until one hears the details. Scientists and scholars of the highest eminence were drawn into the conflict, which has not yet wholly subsided, although the present report must be regarded as quite final in its verdict.

PREFACTORY NOTE

As for Hans himself, he has become the prototype of a host of less distinguished imitators representing every level of animal life, and when last heard from he was still entertaining mystified audiences by his accomplishments.

But the permanent worth of the book is not to be found in its record of popular excitement, interesting as that is. It is a document of the very first consequence in its revelation of the workings of the animal mind as disclosed in the horse. Animal lovers of all kinds, whether scientists or laymen, will find in it material of greatest value for the correct apprehension of animal behavior. Moreover, it affords an illuminating insight into the technique of experimental psychology in its study both of human and animal consciousness. Finally, it contains a number of highly suggestive observations bearing on certain aspects of telepathy and muscle-reading. All things considered, it may fairly be said that few scientific books appeal to so various a range of interests in so vital a way.

Readers who wish to inform themselves of all the personal circumstances in the case may best read the text just as it stands. Those who desire to get at the pith of the matter without reference to its historical settings, may be advised to omit the Introduction by Professor Stumpf of the University of Berlin, together with supplements II, III and IV.

INTRODUCTION

[By C. Stumpf]

A HORSE that solves correctly problems in multiplication and division by means of tapping. Persons of unimpeachable honor, who in the master's absence have received responses, and assure us that in the process they have not made even the slightest sign. Thousands of spectators, horse-fanciers, trick-trainers of first rank, and not one of them during the course of many months' observations are able to discover any kind of regular signal.

That was the riddle. And its solution was found in the unintentional minimal movements of the horse's questioner.

Simple though it may seem, the history of the solution is nevertheless quite complex, and one of the important incidents in it is the appearance of the zoölogist and African traveler, Schillings, upon the scene, and then there is the report of the so-called Hans-Commission of September 12, 1904. And finally there is the scientific investigation, the results of which were published in my report of December 9, 1904.

After a cursory inspection during the month of February, I again called upon Mr. von Osten in July, and asked him to explain to Professor Schumann and me just what method he had used in instructing the horse. We hoped in this way to gain a clue to the

mechanism of Hans's feats. The most essential parts of
the information thus gleaned are summarized in Supplement I. Mr. Schillings came into the courtyard for
the first time about the middle of July. He came as
skeptical as everyone else. But after he, himself, had
received correct responses, he too became convinced, and
devoted much of his time to exhibiting the horse, and
daily brought new guests. To be perfectly frank, at the
time this seemed to us a disturbing factor in the investigation, but now we see that his intervention was a link in
the chain of events which finally led to an explanation.
For it was through him that the fact was established beyond cavil, that the horse was able to respond to strangers
in the master's absence. Heretofore, this had been noted
only in isolated cases. Since it could not be assumed
that a well-known investigator should take it upon himself to mislead the public by intentionally giving signs,
the case necessarily from that time on appeared in the
eyes of others in a light quite different from that in
which ordinary circus-tricks would appear, to which it
bore such a striking external resemblance. No matter
how this state of affairs may have arisen in the course of
years, no matter how it might eventually be explained,—
the quality of the extraordinary would necessarily attach
itself to this particular case, as it did.

Of course, to many persons in the interested public
the result was merely that Schillings, also, was placed in
the category of deceivers. On the other hand there were
reputable scientists who could not dispose of the matter in
that fashion, and these now openly took their stand with
Schillings and declared that they believed in the horse's
ability to think. Zoölogists especially, saw in von Osten's
results evidence of the essential similarity between the

human and the animal mind, which doctrine has been coming more and more into favor since the time of Darwin. Educators were disposed to be convinced, on account of the clever systematic method of instruction which had been used and which had not, till then, been applied in the education of a horse. In addition, there were many details which, it seemed, could not be explained in any other way. So far as I myself was concerned, I was ready to change my views with regard to the nature of animal consciousness, as soon as a careful examination would show that nothing else would explain the facts, except the assumption of the presence of conceptual thinking. I had thought out the process hypothetically, i. e., how one might conceive of the rise of number concepts and arithmetical calculation along the peculiar lines which had been followed in Hans's education, and on the basis of the assumption that the beginnings of conceptual thinking are present in animals. Also, I had too much faith in human nature to fear lest nothing peculiarly human should remain after the art of handling numbers should be shown to be common property with the lower forms. But under no circumstances would I have undertaken to make a public statement in favor of any particular view in this extraordinary case, before a thorough investigation, in accordance with scientific principles, had been made. I expressed this sentiment at the time, and recommended the appointment of an investigating commission (in the " Tag " of September 3, 1904).

The purpose of this commission was misunderstood, and therefore many were disappointed with the report which it published, (Supplement II). Some had been expecting a positive conclusive explanation; the commis-

sion recommended further investigation. Some had
asked for a solution of the question whether or not the
horse was able to think; the commission maintained
neither the one, nor the other. Some had indicated as
the main condition of a satisfactory investigation, that
both Mr. von Osten and Mr. Schillings be excluded from
the tests; this was not done.

But the commission—which, by the way, did not give
itself this name, since it had been delegated by no one—
undoubtedly had the right to formulate its problem as
it saw fit, and this was carefully expressed at the beginning of its report as follows: " The undersigned came
together for the purpose of investigating the question
whether or not there is involved in the feats of the horse
of Mr. von Osten anything of the nature of tricks, that
is, intentional influence or aid on the part of the questioner." It was this preliminary question, and not
whether or not the horse could think, which the commission intended to answer. They proposed to act as a
sort of court of honor for the two gentlemen who had
been attacked. It is only in this light that even the
raison d'être of this body can be understood; for a
scientific commission composed of thirteen men, possessed of varying degrees of scientific preparation, would
have been an absurd travesty, and it will readily be seen
why the two men, who had been attacked, should not be
excluded, since it was they, and primarily Mr. von Osten,
upon whom the observations were to be made.

To be sure the commission did go one step beyond
that which it had proposed to itself, since it added that
it believed that unintentional signs of the kind which are
at present familiar, were also excluded. This led many to
the unwarranted conclusion that the commission had

declared that Hans was able to think. Whereas the thing which might have been logically suggested was that instead of the assumption of the presence of independent thinking, the commission may have had in mind unintentional signs of a kind hitherto unknown. I explained this to a reporter of the "Frankfurter Zeitung" (Mr. A. Gold), who had come to me for information, and in his article he made this hypothesis appear as the most probable one.* Certain statements of the circus-manager Busch, who speaks of a 'connection' of some sort, go to show that other members of the commission held to the view just stated.

But how did it come to pass that the commission should deny completely the presence of intentional signals, while, as regards the unintended, it excluded only those which were of the known sort? The report clearly shows that the decision as to the absence of voluntary signals was

---

* "Frankfurter Zeitung" of September 22, 1904: "Concerning the question whether the horse was given some sort of aid, Professor Stumpf expressed himself freely. He said: 'We were careful to state in our report that the intentional use of the (actual) means of training, on the part of the horse's teacher, is out of the question, ... nor are there involved any of the known kinds of unconscious, involuntary aids. Our task was completed after we had ascertained that no tricks or aids of the traditional sort were being employed'." After some remarks on unconscious habituation and self-training on the part of animals, the writer arrives at the conclusion that "the horse of Mr. von Osten has been educated by its master in the most round-about way, in accordance with a method suited for the development of human reasoning powers, hence in all good faith, to give correct responses by means of tapping with the foot. But what the horse really learned by this wearisome process was something quite different, something that was more in accord with his natural capacities,—he learned to discover by purely sensory aids which are so near the threshold that they are imperceptible for us and even for the teacher, when he is expected to tap with his foot and when he is to come to rest."

based not merely upon the fact that no such signals had been detected by the most expert observers, but also upon the character of the two men who exhibited the horse, upon their behavior during the entire period, and upon the method of instruction which Mr. von Osten had employed. In the case of unintentional signs, on the other hand, one had to deal with the fact with which physiologists and experimental psychologists are especially familiar, viz., that our conscious states, without our willing it—indeed, even in spite of us—are accompanied by bodily changes which very often can be detected only by the use of extremely fine graphic methods. The following is a more general instance: every mother, who detects the lie or divines the wish in the eyes of the child, knows that there are characteristic changes of facial expression, which are, nevertheless, very difficult of definition.*

The commission did not even maintain or believe that unintentional signs within the realm of the senses known to us, were to be excluded. Professor Nagel and I would never have subscribed to any such conclusion. The sentence in question, therefore, could only be interpreted as follows: that signals of the kind that are used in-

---

* "From the productions of the 'thought-readers' we see how slight and seemingly insignificant the unconscious movements may be, which serve as signs for a sensitive re-agent. But in this case no contact is necessary. There would have to be some sort of visible or audible expression on the part of the questioner. No proof for this has as yet been advanced."

How any one possessing the power of logical thought could possibly infer from these words of mine (published in the above-mentioned article in the " Tag "), that I denied the possibility of the occurrence of visual signs, is to me incomprehensible. What I did deny, and still deny, is that up to that time any had been proven to occur.

tentionally in the training of horses, could not have occurred even as unintended signs, for otherwise Mr. Busch would have detected them. And in order to be observed by him it was immaterial whether they were given purposely or not. The same signs, therefore, which as a result of his observations were declared not to be present, could not be assumed to be involved as unintentional.

For my part I am ready to confess that at this time I did not expect to find the involuntary signals, if any such were involved, in the form of movements. I had in mind rather some sort of nasal whisper such as had been invoked by the Danish psychologist A. Lehmann, in order to explain certain cases of so-called telepathy. I could not believe that a horse could perceive movements which escaped the sharp eyes of the circus-manager. To be sure, extremely slight movements may still be perceived after objects at rest have become imperceptible. But one would hardly expect this feat on the part of an animal, who was so deficient in keenness of vision, as we have been led, by those of presumably expert knowledge, to believe of the horse,—one would expect it all the less because Mr. von Osten and Mr. Schillings would move hither and thither in most irregular fashion while the horse was going through his tapping, and would therefore make the perception of minute movements all the more difficult.

Nor was there anything in the exhibitions given at the same time in a Berlin vaudeville by the mare " Rosa," which might have shattered this belief. For, in the case of this rival of Hans, the movements involved were comparatively coarse. The closing signal consisted in bending forward on the part of the one exhibiting the mare, while up to that point he had stood bolt upright. Most persons were not aware of this, because this change in posture cannot be noticed from the front. I happened to sit to the side and caught the movement every time. It was the same that was noted by Dr. Miessner, another member of the commission, (see page 256), but concerning which he did not give me a more complete account. Later I learned through Professor Th. W. Engelmann that the very same movement was employed not long ago, for giving signals to a dog exhibited at Utrecht. This particular movement is very well adapted to commercial purposes, since the spectator always tries to view the performance from a point as nearly in front of the animal and its master as possible, thus making the detection of the trick all the more difficult.

The details of the various experiments made by this commission are given in an excerpt from the records kept by Dr. von Hornbostel, which I showed to a small group of persons a few days after the 12th of September (Supplement III). At that time none of the particulars was published, because the commission wished to wait until some positive statement might be made. The public was merely to be assured that a group of reputable men, from different spheres of life, who could have no purpose in hazarding their reputation, believed that the case was one worthy of careful investigation.

I left Berlin on September 17th and did not return until October 3d. In the meantime Mr. Schillings continued the investigation, and was assisted in part by Mr. Oskar Pfungst, one of my co-workers at the Psychological Institute. For the first time a number of tests were now made in which neither the questioner, nor any of those present knew the answer to the problem. Such tests naturally were the first steps toward a positive investigation. The results were such that Mr. Schillings was led to replace his hypothesis of independent conceptual thinking by one of some kind of suggestion. In this he was strengthened somewhat by having noted the fact that in his questions which he put to the horse, he might proceed as far as to ask the impossible. He has always been ready to offer himself in the tests which have been undertaken since then.

On October 13, 1904, together with the two gentlemen mentioned in the beginning of my report, I began my more detailed investigation, and finished on November 29. We worked for several hours on the average of four times each week. I take this opportunity of giving expression of the recognition which is due to the two gentlemen. They were ready to go to the courtyard in all kinds of weather, at times they went without me, and they always patiently discussed the order and method of the experiments and the results. Dr. von Hornbostel had the important task of keeping the records, and Mr. Pfungst undertook the conduct of the experiments. It was he, who, soon after the blinder-tests disclosed the necessary presence of visual signs, discovered the nature of these signs. Without him we might have shown the horse to be dependent upon visual stimuli in general, but we never would have been able to gain that mass of detail, which makes the case valuable for human psychology. But I am tempted to praise not merely his patience and skill, but also his courage. For we must not believe that Mr. von Osten's horse was a " perfectly gentle " animal. If he stood untied and happened to be excited by some sudden occurrence, he would make that courtyard an unsafe place, and both Mr. Schillings and Mr.

Pfungst suffered from more than one bite. In this connection I would also express my obligations to Count Otto zu Castell-Rüdenhausen, for his frequent intercession on our behalf with the owner of the horse, and for his many evidences of good-will and helpfulness.

After the publication of this report (Supplement IV), there was still some further discussion of the case in societies of various kinds and in the press, but no important objections were raised. A hippologist thought that men of his calling should have been consulted, a telepathist believed that telepathists should have been called in. There was also some further talk of suggestion, will-transference, thought-reading and the occult, but no attempt was made to elucidate these vague terms with reference to their application to the case in hand. Others adhered to the old cry of " fraud," for a share of which Mr. Pfungst now fell heir. There were a few who felt it incumbent upon themselves to preserve their ' priority,' and therefore stated with a show of satisfaction that I had finally ' confessed ' myself to hold their respective points of view. As if there were anything like " confessions " in science! As if mere affirmations, even though sealed and deposited in treasure vaults, had any value with reference to a case in which every manner of supposition had been advanced in lieu of explanation. Why did they wait so long, if they had convincing proof for their position?

And finally there were disappointed Darwinists who expressed fear lest ecclesiastical and reactionary points of view should derive favorable material from the conclusions arrived at in my report. Needless fear. For lovers of truth it must always remain a matter of inconsequence whether anyone is pleased or displeased with the truth, and whether it is enunciated by Aristotle or Haeckel.

Mr. von Osten, however, continued to exhibit Hans, and is probably doing so still, but in what frame of mind, I dare not judge. The spectators continue to look on, they are doubly alert to catch movements, and many of them have learned from Mr. Schillings what kind of movements they are to expect. But these "initiated" ones regularly return and declare that there is nothing in the movements and that they simply could not discover any aids given to the horse. Nothing can so well show how difficult the case is, and how great the need of a thorough exposition of the whole matter, than the account given in the following pages of Mr. Pfungst. Its publication has been delayed on account of the additional tests made in the laboratory, but we have reason to suppose that through these additional tests the work has gained in permanent value. Experimental psychologists will perhaps be greatly interested in the graphic registration of the minute involuntary movements which accompany the thought process, and in the artificial association of a given involuntary movement with a given idea. Likewise the tests on sense-perception in horses, which have led to essential changes in hitherto current views, and the critical review of the comprehensive literature on similar achievements of other animals, will be welcomed by many.

Before closing these introductory remarks, I would make one more statement concerning Mr. von Osten. The reader will notice that the judgment passed upon him in this treatise is placed at the end, whereas in the report of the commission it came first. This was brought about by the change that was made in the way of stating the

problem.   Then the question discussed was whether
'tricks' were involved; now the question is: What is the
mechanism of the process?   The question of the good
faith of the master was taken up once more only because
the facts that were brought to light by the later experimentation seemingly brought forward new grounds for
distrust.   But by placing this discussion toward the end
of our report we wished to indicate that everything that
is said of the present status of facts, is quite independent
of the view taken concerning Mr. von Osten.   Even assuming that the horse had been purposely trained by him
to respond to this kind of signal, the case would still
deserve a place in the annals of science.   For visual signs,
planned and practiced so that they could not only be
more readily perceived by the animal than by man, but
could be transferred from their inventor to others without
any betrayal of the secret,—this would be an extraordinary invention, and Mr. von Osten would then be a
fraud, but also a genius of first rank.

In truth he probably was neither, but I was brief
in my report, for otherwise I would have been obliged
to go into more detail than the case warranted.   And a
judgment passed upon a human personality is quite a
different matter from a judgment upon a horse.   If it is
unscientific to make unqualified statements concerning
a horse after the performance of only a few experimental
tests, it is certainly an unwarranted thing to pass a moral
judgment upon a man upon the basis of meagre material.
Anyone who would assume the rôle of judge should bear
in mind that here too we have more than a hundredfold
the material which they could bring forward, and among
it some which, if taken alone, would be more unfavorable
than any that they had.   But here all things should be

weighed together, and not in isolation. A former instructor of mathematics in a German gymnasium, a pas-
sionate horseman and hunter, extremely patient and at
the same time highly irrascible, liberal in permitting the
use of the horse for days at a time and again tyrannical
in the insistence upon foolish conditions, clever in his
method of instruction and yet at the same time possessing
not even the slightest notion of the most elementary conditions of scientific procedure,—all this, and more, goes
to make up the man. He is fanatic in his conviction, he
has an eccentric mind which is crammed full of theories
from the phrenology of Gall to the belief that the horse
is capable of inner speech and thereby enunciates inwardly the number as it proceeds with the tapping. From
theories such as these, and on the basis of all sorts of
imagined emotional tendencies in the horse, he also
managed to formulate an explanation for the failure of
the tests in which none of the persons present knew the
answer to the problem given the horse, and also for the
failure of those tests in which the large blinders were
applied. And he would often interfere with or hinder
other tests which, according to his point of view, were
likely to lead us astray. And yet, when the first tests
with the blinders did turn out as unmistakably sheer
failures, there was such genuine surprise, such tragi-
comic rage directed against the horse, that we finally
believed that his views in the matter would be changed
beyond a doubt. " The gentlemen must admit," he said
at the time, " that after seeing the objective success of
my efforts at instruction, I was warranted in my belief
in the horse's power of independent thought." Nevertheless, upon the following day he was as ardent an ex-

ponent of the belief in the horse's intelligence as he ever had been.

And finally, after I could no longer keep from him the results of our investigation, I received a letter from him in which he forbade further experimentation with the horse. The purpose of our inquiries, he said, had been to corroborate his theories. On account of his withdrawal of the horse a few experimental series unfortunately could not be completed, but happily the major portion of our task had been accomplished.

THE HORSE OF MR. VON OSTEN

CHAPTER I

THE PROBLEM OF ANIMAL CONSCIOUSNESS AND "CLEVER HANS"

IF we would appreciate the interest that has been aroused everywhere by the wonderful horse solving arithmetical problems, we must first consider briefly the present state of the problem of animal consciousness.* Animal consciousness cannot be directly gotten at, and the psychologist must therefore seek to appreciate it on the basis of the animal's behavior and with the assistance of conceptions borrowed from human psychology. Hence it is that animal psychology rests upon uncertain foundations with the result that the fundamental principles have been repeatedly questioned and agreement has not yet been attained. The most important of these questions is, "Does the animal possess consciousness, and is it like the human consciousness?" Comparative psychologists divide into three groups on this question.

The one group allows consciousness to the lower forms, but emphasizes the assertion that between the animal and the human consciousness there is an impassable

---

* Since the present treatise is intended for the larger public, this brief resumé will probably be welcome to many.

gap. The animal may have sensations and memory-images of sensations which may become associated in manifold combinations. Both sensations and memory images are believed to be accompanied by conditions of pleasure and of pain (so-called sensuous feelings), and these in turn, become the mainsprings of desire. The possession of memory gives the power of learning through experience. But with this, the inventory of the content of animal consciousness is exhausted. The ability to form concepts * and with their aid to make judgments and draw conclusions is denied the lower forms. All the higher intellectual, æsthetic and moral feelings, as well as volition guided by motives, are also denied. Among the ancients this view was held by Aristotle and the Stoics; and following them it was taught by the Christian Church. It pervaded all mediæval philosophy, which grew out of the teachings of Aristotle and the Church. It is this philosophy, in the form of Neo-Thomism, which still obtains in the Catholic world.

During the 17th century, even though temporarily, another conception of the consciousness of lower forms came to prevail and was introduced by Descartes, the " Father " of modern philosophy. Far more radical than the earlier conception, it denied to animals not only the

---

* Ideas are copies of former sensations, feelings and other psychic experiences and retain also the accidental signs which belonged to those earlier experiences. They are images in the concrete, such as the memory of a certain horse in a certain definite situation . . . . . say a well-fed, long-tailed one standing at a manger. A concept, on the other hand, is a mental construct which has its rise in ideas, or memory-images, in that their essential characteristics are abstracted. For this reason the concept has not a definite image-content. (Thus the thought of " horse " in general, is a concept. Not so the thought of a certain individual horse,—— that is an idea, with a definite image-content.)

power of abstract thought, but every form of psychic life whatever, and reduced the lower form to a machine, which automatically reacted upon external stimuli. This daring view, however, prevailed for only a comparatively short period; but owing to the opposition which it aroused, it gave a tremendous impetus to the study of animal consciousness. Most of the great philosophers following Descartes, such as Locke, Leibniz, Kant, and Schopenhauer, however greatly they may have differed in other points, in this one returned to the Aristotelian point of view.

A third belief avers that animal and human consciousness do not differ in essentials, but only in degree. This conclusion is regularly arrived at by those who regard so-called abstract thought itself, as simply a play of individual sensations and sensation-images, as did the French and British associationists (Condillac and the Mills). The superiority of man accordingly consisted in his ability to form more intricate ideational complexes. Again, this conception of the essential similarity of the human and the animal psyche has also always been arrived at by the materialists (from Epicurus to C. Vogt and Büchner) who impute reason to the animal form as well as to man. The same position is, furthermore, taken by the evolutionists, including those who do not subscribe to the doctrines of materialism. It has almost become dogma with them that there exists an unbroken chain of psychic life from the lowest protozoa to man. Haeckel, preëminently, though not always convincingly, sought to establish such a graded series and thus to bridge the chasm between the human and the animal consciousness.

Two tendencies, therefore, are discernible in animal

psychology. The one seeks to remove the animal psyche farther away from the human, the other tries to bring the two closer together. It is undoubtedly true that many acts of the lower forms reveal nothing of the nature of conceptual thinking. But that others might thus be interpreted cannot be denied. But need they be thus interpreted?—There lies the dispute. A single incontrovertible fact which would fulfil this demand, [i.e., proof of conceptual thinking], would, at a stroke, decide the question in favor of those who ascribe the power of thought to the lower forms.

At last the thing so long sought for, was apparently found: A horse that could solve arithmetical problems—an animal which, thanks to long training, mastered not merely rudiments, but seemingly arrived at a power of abstract thought and which surpassed, by far, the highest expectations of the greatest enthusiast.

And now what was it that this wonderful horse could do? The reader may accompany us to an exhibition which was given daily before a select company at about the noon hour in a paved courtyard surrounded by high apartment houses in the northern part of Berlin. No fee was ever taken. The visitor might walk about freely and if he wished, might closely approach the horse and its master, a man between sixty and seventy years of age. His white head was covered with a black, slouch hat. To his left the stately animal, a Russian trotting horse, stood like a docile pupil, managed not by means of the whip, but by gentle encouragement and frequent reward of bread or carrots. He would answer correctly, nearly all of the questions which were put to him in German. If he understood a question, he immediately indicated this by a nod of the head; if he failed to grasp its import, he communicated the fact by a shake of the head. We were told that the questioner had to confine himself to a certain vocabulary, but this was comparatively rich and the horse widened its scope daily without special instruction, but by simple contact with his environment. His master, to be sure, was usually present whenever questions were put to the horse by others, but in the course of time, he gradually responded to a greater and greater number of persons. Even though Hans did not appear as willing and reliable in the case of strangers as in the case of his own master, this might easily be explained by the lack of authoritativeness on their part and of affection on the part of Hans, who for the last four years had had intercourse only with his master.

Our intelligent horse was unable to speak, to be sure. His chief mode of expression was tapping with his right forefoot. A good deal was also expressed by means of movements of the head. Thus " yes " was expressed by a nod, " no " by a deliberate movement from side to side; and " upward," "upper," " downward," " right," " left," were indicated by turning the head in these directions. In this he showed an astonishing ability to put himself in the place of his visitors. Upon being asked which arm was raised by a certain gentleman opposite him, Hans promptly answered by a movement to the right, even though seen from his own side, it would appear to be the left. Hans would also walk toward the persons or things that he was asked to point out, and he would bring from a row of colored cloths, the piece of the particular color demanded. Taking into account his limited means of expression, his master had translated a large number of concepts into numbers; e. g. :—the letters of the alphabet, the tones of the scale, and the names of the playing cards were indicated by taps. In the case of playing cards one tap meant "ace," two taps "king," three "queen," etc.

Let us turn now to some of his specific accomplishments. He had, apparently, completely mastered the cardinal numbers from 1 to 100 and the ordinals to 10, at least. Upon request he would count objects of all sorts, the persons present, even to distinctions of sex. Then hats, umbrellas, and eyeglasses. Even the mechanical activity of tapping seemed to reveal a measure of intelligence. Small numbers were given with a slow tapping of the right foot. With larger numbers he would increase his speed, and would often tap very rapidly right from the start, so that one might have gained the impression that knowing that he had a large number to tap, he desired to hasten the monotonous activity. After the final tap, he would return his right foot—which he used in his counting—to its original position, or he would make the final count with a very energetic tap of the left foot,—to underscore it, as it were. "Zero" was expressed by a shake of the head.

But Hans could not only count, he could also solve problems in arithmetic. The four fundamental processes were entirely familiar to him. Common fractions he changed to decimals, and vice versa; he could solve problems in mensuration—and all with such ease that it was difficult to follow him if one had become somewhat rusty in these branches. The following problems are illustrations of the kind he solved.* "How much is $\frac{2}{5}$ plus $\frac{1}{2}$?" Answer: $\frac{9}{10}$. (In the case of all fractions Hans would first tap the numerator, then the denominator; in

* All examples mentioned are cited from extant works of various observers.

this case, therefore, first 9, then 10). Or again: " I have a number in mind. I subtract 9, and have 3 as a remainder. What is the number I had in mind?"—12. " What are the factors of 28? "—Thereupon Hans tapped consecutively 2, 4, 7, 14, 28. " In the number 365287149 I place a decimal point after the 8. How many are there now in the hundreds place? "—5. " How many in the ten thousandths place? "—9. It will be noticed, therefore, that he was able to operate with numbers far exceeding 100, indeed he could manipulate those of six places. We were told that this, however, was no longer arithmetical computation in the true sense of the term; Hans merely knew after the analogy of 10 and 100 that the thousands take the fourth place, the ten-thousands the fifth, etc. If an error entered into Hans' answer, he could nearly always correct it immediately upon being asked: " By how many units did you go wrong? "

Hans, furthermore, was able to read the German readily, whether written or printed. Mr. von Osten, however, taught him only the small letters, not the capitals. If a series of placards with written words were placed before the horse, he could step up and point with his nose to any of the words required of him. He could even spell some of the words. This was done by the aid of a table devised by Mr. von Osten, in which every letter of the alphabet, as well as a number of diphthongs had an appropriate place which the horse could designate by means of a pair of numbers. Thus in the fifth horizontal row " s " had first place; " sch " second, " ss," third, etc.; so that the horse would indicate the letter " s " by treading first 5, then 1, " sch," by 5 and 2, " ss " by 5 and 3. Upon being asked " What is this woman holding in her hand? " Hans spelled without hesitation: 3, 2; 4, 6; 3, 7; i. e., "Schirm" (parasol). At another time a picture of a horse standing at a manger was shown him and he was asked, "What does this represent?" He promptly spelled "Pferd" (horse) and then "Krippe" (manger).

He, moreover, gave evidence of an excellent memory. In passing we might also mention that he knew the value of all the German coins. But most astonishing of all was the following: Hans carried the entire yearly calendar in his head; he could give you not only the date for each day without having been previously taught anew, but he could give you the date of any day you might mention. He could also answer such inquiries as this: "If the eighth day of a month comes on Tuesday, what is the date for the following Friday?" He could tell the time to the minute by a watch and could answer off-hand the question, "Between what figures is the small hand of a watch at 5 minutes after half-past seven?" or, "How many minutes has the large hand to travel between seven minutes after a quarter past the hour, and three quarters past?" Tasks that were given him but once would be repeated correctly upon request. The sentence: "Brücke und Weg sind vom Feinde besetzt" (The bridge and the road are held by the enemy), was given to Hans one day and upon the following day he tapped consecutively the 58 numbers which were necessary for a correct response. He recognized persons after having seen them but once—yes, even their photographs taken in previous years and bearing but slight resemblance.

A corresponding high degree of sensory activity seemed to accompany these astonishing feats of memory and reason. Although the horse is not usually credited with a very keen sense of vision, Hans was able to count the windows of distant houses and the street urchins climbing about on neighboring roofs. He had an ear for the most subtle nuances of the voice. He caught every word,—no matter how softly it was spoken—so that we were not allowed to whisper the answer to a problem, even when standing at a distance of several yards, since it would be equivalent—so Mr. von Osten declared—to giving the result to the horse.

Musical ability also comes into the category of Hans' accomplishments. He possessed, not only an absolute tone consciousness—a gift granted to few of us in the human world—which enabled him to recognize a note sounded or sung to him as c, d, etc. (within the once accented scale of c-major), but also an infallible feeling for intervals, and could therefore determine whether two tones, sounded simultaneously, composed a third or fifth, etc. Without difficulty he analyzed compound clangs into their components; he indicated their agreeableness or disagreeableness and could inform us which tones must be eliminated to make consonance out of dissonance. C, d and e were given simultaneously and Hans was asked: "Does that sound pleasant?" He shook his head. "What tone must be omitted to make it pleasant?" Hans trod twice—indicating tone "d." When the seventh chord, d-f-a-c, was sounded, he shook his head disapprovingly. He evidently was old-fashioned in his musical tastes and not agreeably disposed toward modern music, so he indicated by tapping that the seventh, c, would have to be eliminated; thus changing the seventh chord to a minor chord in order to obtain harmony. When asked what tones might not be given simultaneously with the fourth and sixth, Hans indicated consecutively the third, fifth and seventh; that the first might be added, he was ready to admit. Finally, he was familiar with not less than thirteen melodies and their time.

Not only in the high degree of development of the senses and the intellect, but also in that of the feeling and the will, did Hans possess a decided individuality. Being of a high-strung and nervous temperament and governed by moods, he evinced strong likes and dislikes, and frequently displayed an annoying stubbornness,—a fact often dwelt upon by Mr. von Osten. He had never felt the whip, and therefore often persisted in wilfully answering the simplest questions incorrectly and a moment later would solve, with the greatest ease, some of the most difficult problems. Whenever any one asked a question without himself knowing the answer, Hans would indulge in all sorts of sport at the questioner's expense. We were told that the sensitive animal could easily perceive the questioner's ignorance and would therefore lose confidence in, and respect for, him. It was felt to be desirable, however, to have just such cases with correct responses. Often, too, Hans would persist in giving what seemed an incorrect reply, but which was later discovered to be correct. On the other hand it was useless to try to get answers upon topics of which he knew nothing. Thus he ignored questions put in French or Latin and became fidgety, thereby showing the genuineness of his achievements; but upon topics with which he was familiar he could not be led astray. Indeed, there was nothing but language lacking to make him almost human and the intelligent animal was declared by experienced educators to be at about the stage of development of a child of 13 or 14 years.

This wonderful horse, which in the opinion of its friends was the means of deciding in the affirmative the old, old, question of the rationality of the lower forms and thus changing radically the existing Weltanschauung, aroused world-wide interest. A flood of articles appeared in the newspapers and magazines, two monograph [1,2] attempts at explanation were devoted to him.* He was made the subject of popular couplets, and his name was sung on the vaudeville stage. He appeared upon picture post-cards and upon liquor labels, and his popularity was shown by his reincarnation in the form of children's playthings. Many personages of note who had seen the horse's exhibitions, declared, some of them in public statements, that they were now convinced. Among these, besides Mr. Schillings, were naturalists of note; e. g.: the African explorer Prof. G. Schweinfurth, Dr. Heinroth and Dr. Schäff, the director of the zoölogical garden in Hanover; there were likewise horse-fanciers of first-rank, such as General Zobel, and the well-known hippological writer Major R. Schoenbeck. Again, the well-known zoölogist, K. Möbius, writing in the "National-zeitung" declared he was convinced of the horse's power to count and to solve arithmetical problems. He also said that he believed the horse's memory and acute power of sense-discrimination to be at the root of the matter. Those who gleaned all their knowledge of the horse from newspaper reading were satisfied to arrest judgment. or, on the other hand, became indignant at the supposed imposition on the part of the gentleman of leisure and at the gullibility of the public. Some would of course attempt explanations on the basis of older facts. Here we have two points of view.

* The works referred to in the text are to be found listed on pages 267 ff.

Some tried to explain the whole thing on the basis of purely mechanical memory and would thus allow the title " learned " but not " intelligent " Hans. If, for instance, he was able to indicate the component of a clang of three tones, it was not because he had the power to analyze the tone-complex, but because he was able to see the stops of the harmonica and was accustomed to give one tap for every stop which was closed. If he was able to tell time by the watch, it was not because he read it, but because he was always asked at the same hour of the day (which, of course, was contrary to fact) and because he had learned by heart the necessary number of taps. They also said that his manifold arithmetical achievements were merely the expression of a remarkable memory; that in the animal brain, lying fallow for centuries, there was stored up a tremendous amount of energy, which here had been suddenly released. They justified their point by calling to mind, in this connection, the wonderful memory of primitive races. The authors of the two monographs already mentioned, Zell and Freund, adopted this ' mnemotechnic ' interpretation, and the latter considered that he had disposed definitely of the problem in designating the horse—a " four-legged computing machine."

Another group would not even allow Hans the glory of a wonderful memory. He knew nothing. Rather was he to be regarded as a stupid Hans, and totally dependent upon signs or helps given by his master. Only a very few believed, however, that such signs—the nature of which was quite unknown or regarding which only vague unsubstantiated suppositions were advanced —were given unintentionally. Most of the critics openly averred that we here had to do with intentional control,

in other words, with tricks. But not only did stupid
orthodoxy dispose of the matter in this way, but also the
enlightened, who believe everything unusual to be contrary to reason. They put the Hans problem on a level
with spiritualism, and were convinced that if the veil
were removed a crass imposition would be revealed.
Professional trainers who regarded themselves as well
informed did not hesitate to give expression to this same
view, even though they had observed Hans inad-
equately or not at all.

The defenders of this second point of view were not
at a loss to point out the signs supposed to be given to
Hans. One of these believed he had discovered the
primary means for giving these signs in the slouch hat
of Mr. von Osten. It was no accident, they said, that
Mr. Schillings wore a slouch hat when he experimented
with the horse. It is sufficient to note that Mr. Schillings was usually bare-headed or wore only a cap when
he tested the horse. Another accused, in like fashion,
the long coat of the experimenter; a third, who " had
had opportunity to observe Hans on several occasions,"
declared with equal certainty that the cue lay in the
movements of the hand as it was thrust into the pocket
filled with carrots. One circus-star declared, that the
trick lay in eye movements, another such star declared it
lay in the movements of the hand. A sixth discovered
that the signs were " manifold " and adds, " to be sure, the
trainer must have a fund of such signs in order to prevent
embarrassment." Such a hypothesis is itself, it would
seem, one of embarrassment. On the other hand, there
were many first-class observers who vainly tried to discover regularly recurring signs; among them the only
professional trainer,—who had devoted any satisfactory

length of time to the horse and had also sought diligently for the signs in question—said, " I was fully convinced that I would be able to explain the problem in this way, but I was mistaken." The president of the " Internationale Artisten Genossenschaft," a person who knew all the usual means of control in trick performances, went over to the other side as a result of his observations.

There were others who sought for auditory signs. The opinion was expressed that " Hans was unable to answer the simplest question such as ' What is two plus three? ' whenever the questioner's tone of voice differed from that of the master's." Another put chief stress upon the changing inflection; furthermore, a " high degree of auditory sensitivity " was often offered in explanation.

The sense of smell was also made to bear some burdens. With its help, for instance, Hans was believed to be able to recognize the photograph of some one present, supposing, of course, that the person had carried the picture about with him, thus allowing it to be impregnated with his peculiar personal odor. One even suggested that the heat radiating from the questioner's body and the electric stimulus conducted underground to Hans's foot were sufficient explanation for his remarkable feats.

Even the so-called N-rays, of one-day fame, which were supposed to radiate from the human brain when in activity, were offered as a solution. A similar thing may have been in the mind of the " natural philosopher " who even after the publication of the December report, wrote as follows in one of the journals: " On the basis of most careful control, I have come to the conclusion, that the brain of the horse receives the thought-waves which radiate from the brain of his master; for mental work is,

according to the judgment of science, physical work."
Of the same character are the explanations of two others,
one of whom declares that Hans was acting " under the
magnetic influence of man ", while the other declared that
" hypnotic suggestion is involved ", and, ignoring attested
facts, tells us that, " The horse can execute the commands of another only when the master, with whom it is
' en rapport ', wills that it shall obey." We may close
the catalogue of explanations with one more, which, in
spite of its vagueness, found many defenders, viz: suggestion. Without defining this conception more specifically and without the slightest notion of the peculiar difficulties which it involves (L. Loewenfeld in his " Handbuch des Hypnotismus " [Wiesbaden, 1901, pp. 35ff.]
cites twenty different definitions of the term given by as
many authors) a critic writes: " The astounding phenomenon of an animal apparently possessing human reason
is to be attributed solely to suggestion ". Having referred to a dog trained for the vaudeville-stage, the gentleman concludes that, " our intelligent horse, as well as
the dog, is simply of fine nervous organization and hence
highly susceptible to suggestions ".

What was to be done, with this mass of conflicting explanations? Everyone considered his own opinion the
only correct one, without, however, being able to convince anyone else. The need here was not simple affirmation, but proof.

CHAPTER II

EXPERIMENTS AND OBSERVATIONS

A. Experimental Conditions

THE observations on the horse under ordinary conditions would have been quite insufficient for arriving at a decision as to the tenability of the several possible explanations. For this purpose experimentation with controlled conditions was necessary.

It was necessary, first, that the place in which the experiments were performed should be guarded against sources of error and interruptions. Several difficulties stood in the way of the removal of the horse to a more convenient place. Therefore, a large canvas tent was erected within the courtyard of Mr. von Osten. This afforded the necessary isolation without hindering the free movements of the horse. After the essential part of the experiment had been completed and the problem had been practically solved, experimentation was sometimes conducted in the open courtyard. A number of the experiments were also performed in the horse's stall.

The choice of proper persons to experiment with the horse required careful consideration. In so far as observations were to be made upon the questioner, Mr. von Osten was of course indispensable. But to obviate every objection he, as well as Mr. Schillings, had to be excluded from the greater part of the experiments, and other persons had to be selected who could learn to handle the horse.   Now one would have thought that the horse would respond to any moderately efficient examiner.   But as a matter of fact it was found that the horse would not react at all in the case of the greater number of persons. Again, in the case of others he would respond once or twice, but would then cease.   All told, Hans responded more or less readily to forty persons, but it was only when he worked with Mr. von Osten or with Mr. Schillings, that his responses were at all dependable.   For this reason I undertook to befriend the horse, and by happy chance it came to pass in a short time he responded as readily to my questions as to those of the two gentlemen.   In a few of these experiments the Count zu Castell, Count R. von Matuschka and Mr. Schillings undertook the rôle of questioner.   Where these are not mentioned in the results here published, I myself did the questioning.

With regard to the number of experiments and their performance, the following precautions were observed. A sufficiently large number of tests was made in each series in order to obviate the possibility of the contention that the horse's errors were due to chance.   The conditions of experimentation were such that the further contention that he happened to be tired or otherwise indisposed, whenever the reactions seemed to be inadequate, could not be offered.   The possibility of confusing the horse by means of unwonted conditions also had to be avoided.   For this reason it was necessary to alternate the trial in which procedure was with the knowledge of the answer on the part of the questioner, with the trial in which the procedure was without such knowledge.   Such precautions had hitherto been neglected, and therefore those negative results which had been occasionally obtained in single trials, could not claim objective validity, even though the persons making the tests were subjectively convinced.

The course of the experiments was determined by the nature of the problem itself. By means of a very simple test it was possible to discover whether or not Hans was able to think independently. He was confronted with problems in which the procedure was without knowledge of the answer on the part of the questioner. If under these conditions he could respond with the correct answer—which could be the result of a rational process only—then the conclusion that he could think independently, was warranted. The examination would be closed and Mr. von Osten would be justified in all he claimed for the horse. If, however, Hans should fail in this test, then the conclusion that he could think was by no means warranted, but rather the inference that he was dependent upon certain stimuli received from the questioner or the environment. Further investigation would be for the purpose of discovering the nature of these stimuli.

To ascertain by means of which sense organ or organs the horse might receive these necessary stimuli, the method of elimination was employed. We began by excluding visual stimuli by means of a pair of very large blinders. Should this investigation be without results, then we would proceed to test the sense of hearing. The elimination of auditory stimulations would be more difficult, because ear-caps or the closing of the passage by means of cotton would not give sufficient assurance that the sound-waves were being interrupted, even if the horse were docile enough to suffer these appliances. Thereupon would follow the testing of the sense of smell and of the skin-senses. And finally there might be involved another still unknown sense, such as seems to exist in the lower animal-forms. The reader therefore can readily see that the investigation might possibly have become very complex, and that the investigator had to be prepared for all of these possibilities.

The results of the experiments and the essential circumstances under which they were conducted, were in every case recorded immediately.

It goes without saying that in the final formulation of the results, all values—including those which were not consonant with the majority—were to be used.

B. Experimental Results

During the course of these experiments Hans wore his accustomed trappings, i. e., a girdle, light headgear and snaffle, and he either stood alone, untied, or was held loosely by the bridle either by the questioner or (though only in a few instances) by his attendant. The questioner always stood to the right of the horse, as Mr. von Osten had been accustomed to do. As reward for correct responses Hans received from the questioner *—and from him only—a bit of bread or carrot, and at times also a square of sugar. Never was a whip applied. From time to time the horse was led about the courtyard or was allowed to run loose in order to secure the needful respite. Besides myself there was usually present Prof. Stumpf and Dr. von Hornbostel, who kept the records, and frequently also Mr. von Osten. Several times I worked alone with the horse. The results obtained in the horse's stall were in no respect different from those got in the

---

* The expressions *questioner* and *experimenter* are used interchangeably in this treatise.

course of the experiments carried on in the courtyard. Whenever a doubt arose as to the number of taps made by the horse (though this did not frequently occur), then the series in question was immediately repeated.

In this report of the results of our experiments, the reader must bear in mind that it was impossible to adhere to that order and distribution of tests which we are wont to require in the case of psychophysical experiments conducted under regular laboratory conditions. All sorts of difficulties had to be overcome: unfavorable weather, the crowds of curious ones, certain peculiarities of the horse —such as shying whenever the wind rippled the canvas of the tent—and last but not least, the idiosyncrasies of Mr. von Osten who repeatedly attempted to interrupt the progress of the experiments.

Since it was evident that different kinds of processes were involved in solving the problems and since the solutions would be indicated by tapping, or by movements of the head, or by walking over to the object to be designated, the results of these three sets of experiments have been grouped under three corresponding heads.

I. Problems solved by tapping

The following tests were made in which the method was such that when the problem was presented to the horse, the correct solution was known to none of those present, least of all to the questioner. This method we shall designate in the following report as " procedure without knowledge " whereas we shall call the method in which the answer was known to the questioner, " procedure with knowledge ".

In order to discover if the horse could read numbers,

a series of cards on which numerals were blazoned, were exposed to the horse's view in such a way that none of those present was able to see them, and the horse was asked to tap the numbers as they were shown.   This experiment was repeated at different times and in all there were 49 tests in which procedure was without knowledge, and 42 in which procedure was with knowledge.   In the case of the former there were 8% correct responses, whereas in the case of the latter 98% of the answers were right.   As an example of the course which the series tended to take, we insert the following, in which Mr. von Osten himself acted as questioner.

Method.	No. exposed.	No. tapped.
Without knowledge	8	14
With "	8	8
Without "	4	8
With "	4	4
Without "	7	9
With "	7	7
Without "	10	17
With "	10	10
Without "	3	9
With "	3	3 etc.

Whenever the questioner knew the solution, nearly all of the horse's answers were correct; but when the answers were unknown to the questioner, the horse's responses were, with only a few exceptions, quite unsuccessful.   Since the few exceptional cases must be regarded as fortuitous, the conclusion is warranted that the horse was unable to read numerals without assistance.

In order to discover whether the horse could read words such as " Hans " or " Stall " or the names of colors, they were written upon placards and hung up in a row before the horse in such a way that the questioner could see the individual word but could not immediately recognize the particular place that each one occupied in the series. The horse was then asked: " Upon which placard is the word ' Hans '?, " On which is the word ' Stall '? ", etc. In order to make sure, he was required to repeat each answer.

Then the experimenter would determine for himself the place of the word in the series and would ask the question again. Fourteen such tests, in which the procedure was with knowledge on the part of the questioner, were interspersed with twelve in which the procedure was without such knowledge. With the latter there were no correct responses, whereas in the cases of procedure with knowledge 100% of the answers were correct. Evidently the horse could not read words.

Three words were thereupon whispered in his ear, which he was asked to spell in accordance with the method described on page 21. Since he had to indicate first the row, and then the place in the row occupied by the letter, it took two answers to indicate the position of each letter. I acted as questioner. The ordering of the table of letters was unknown to me, except the position of the letter " a ", which naturally came first, and the place of the letter " s ", concerning whose position I had purposely inquired. The words chosen for this experiment were " Arm ", " Rom " (Rome) and " Hans ". The horse responded incorrectly in the case of every letter which was unknown to the questioner. " A " and " s " alone were given correctly. Thus in spelling the word " Rom " the horse responded with the series 3, 4; 3, 4; 5, 4; 5, 4; i. e. " jjst ", instead of the correct series: 4, 6; 4, 2; 3, 7. I later selected three other words, the spelling of which involved the tapping of thirty-two numbers on the part of Hans, and whose position I had carefully ascertained beforehand. When these were given to the horse to spell, he responded promptly without a single error. Evidently Hans was unable to spell without assistance of some sort from the questioner.

The horse's reputed aptitude in computation was tested in the following way. Mr. von Osten whispered a number in the horse's ear so that none of the persons present could hear. Thereupon I did likewise. Hans was asked to add the two. Since each of the experimenters knew only his own number, the sum, if known to anyone, could be known to Hans alone. Every such test was immediately repeated with the result known to the experimenters. In 31 tests in which the method was procedure without knowledge, 3 of the horse's answers were correct, whereas in the 31 tests in which the method was procedure with knowledge, 29 of his responses were correct. Since the three correct answers in the cases in which procedure was without knowledge evidently were accidental, the results of this series of experiments show that Hans was unable to solve arithmetical problems.

For the purpose of discovering whether the horse could at least count, the Russian kindergarten device, which Mr. von Osten had used in training, was utilized. The machine was placed before the horse, but the experimenter turned his back upon it. Before each test, a number of balls were pushed to one side and Hans's problem was to indicate the number thus separated. Each test was repeated with procedure with knowledge. Of eight such experiments Hans responded successfully every time procedure was with knowledge but failed every time procedure was without knowledge. Thus 7 balls were at one time designated as 9 and later as 14, while 6 were at first designated as 12, and later as 10. Since all these errors could not be accounted for on the ground of miscounts on the part of the horse, it was evident that Hans is quite unable to count.

The memory-test was conducted in the following manner. In the absence of the questioner a number or the name of some day of the week was spoken to the horse. The experimenter would then return and question him. Of 10 responses 2 were correct, 8 incorrect. Among the correct answers were the number 3, a number which, as we shall see, Hans was prone to give under all sorts of conditions, and which therefore meant very little when given as a correct response. The number 2, on the other hand, was consecutively indicated by 7, 9, 5, and 3, 8 was given as 5, 6, 4, and 6, consecutively; and finally Wednesday was indicated as the fourteenth day of the week. After this we undertook the test the horse's far-famed knowledge of the calendar. Dates, such as Feb. 29, Nov. 12, etc., were given to Hans and he was asked to indicate on which day of the week they fell. Sunday was to be indicated by 1, Monday by 2, etc. Of 14 such tests, 10 were unsuccessful, 4 successful. But in the case of these 4 something very interesting occurred. It happened that during this series the keeper of the horse was present, and he happened to know the days on which these dates fell,—as he himself testified. The dates in question were also little more than a week or so from the day of the experiment, so they could easily be determined. But as soon as we took more remote dates both man and beast were hopelessly lost. It was certain that Hans had no knowledge of the calendar. It is needless to say anything of his supposed knowledge of cards and coins. Hans plainly was incapable of the astonishing feats of memory which had been claimed for him.

Finally we investigated Hans' musical ability. In a room adjoining the horse's stall there was a small harmonica, which spanned the once accented octave. On this one or more tones were played. The horse was required to indicate the tone played, the number of tones played and their relation to one another. For testing his general hearing 20 tests were given in which the method was procedure without knowledge. Of the responses only one was correct, and that one was the tone e, for which the proper response was three taps, but we must bear in mind what has already been said of the number 3. The tone b was indicated by 11 taps, although Hans had only learned a scale of one octave and therefore could respond to only seven tones. In the tests in which the method was procedure with knowledge, he again, without exception, was successful. Similar results were obtained in the analysis of compound clangs. In the cases of procedure without knowledge (although the experimenter here knew the correct responses, he purposely refrained from thinking of them) not a single response was correct; while in the cases of procedure with knowledge, all but one were correct. The following were typical responses: Three tones were played and the question was asked, "How many tones were played?" Hans responded first with 4 taps and then with 1. The tones c, e, g, a, (1, 3, 5, 6) were struck and the question asked, "Which tone must be eliminated to make the complex a chord?" In the tests in which the method had been procedure with knowledge, this question had always been answered correctly, but when procedure was without knowledge the responses were first 13, a tone which does not exist for Hans, then 2, a tone which was not given in the clang to be analyzed, and finally 3, which was not the discordant tone. Hans's far-famed musical ability was an illusion.

Taking the results of all the tests into consideration, we find that in the case of procedure with knowledge, 90 to 100% of the responses of the various series were correct, whereas, in those series of procedure without knowledge 10%, at most, of the responses were correct. Under the conditions prevailing during these latter tests, even these 10% must be regarded as due to chance. To be sure Mr. Grabow, a member of the school board and an enthusiastic follower of Mr. von Osten (Zeitschrift für Pädagogische Psychologie, Pathologie und Hygiene, Berlin, 1904, Jahrg. 6, Heft. 6, S. 470), mentions a large number of successful tests, which were supposedly made in accordance with the method of procedure without knowledge. A thorough analysis of his experiments was not possible, because the conditions under which they were conducted were not adequately specified. But I have no doubt that the successful responses of the horse were due solely to the absence of precautionary measures. I, too, could cite a number of seemingly correct responses which demonstrably were due to the absence of adequate precautionary measures. I therefore repeat: Hans can neither read, count nor make calculations. He knows nothing of coins or cards, calendars or clocks, nor can he respond, by tapping or otherwise, to a number spoken to him but a moment before. Finally, he has not a trace of musical ability.

After all this experimentation it was evident that the horse was unable to work alone, but was dependent upon certain stimuli from its environment. The question therefore arose: does the horse get these stimuli while the question is being put, or during his responses, i. e., during the process of tapping.

If Mr. von Osten's opinion was correct, then the process of questioning played an important part in the success of the experiment. Of course, as he said, it was not necessary to ask the question aloud; it was sufficient —curiously enough—that it be inwardly spoken, thanks to the horse's extraordinary auditory sensitivity. If, however, conditions were made such that the auditory sense was eliminated, then the animal would be unable to respond. Such a theory is not quite as absurd as it might seem at first blush. For Hansen and Lehmann have shown that an acute auditory organ is able to respond to such delicate stimulation as is involved in the softest whisper, or even in the so-called nasal whisper in which the lips are tightly closed.[3] They have attempted thus to explain any modes of supposed " thought-transference ", (cf. page 7). Since experts on horses agree that the horse has acute auditory sensitivity, Mr. von Osten seized upon this fact and tried to establish his theory in the following manner. No response was successfully made on the part of the horse, he said, when the sound waves caused by his (Mr. von Osten's) inner speech were deflected from the ear of the horse. This was the case when he closed nose and mouth while inwardly putting the question, or deflected the waves from the horse's ear by means of a placard held before his mouth while speaking, or finally by applying lined ear-muffs to the horse's ears. If, on the other hand, he closed only his nose and not his mouth while thus inwardly putting the question, or if he held the placard so that there was a possibility of deflecting the sounds to the horse's ear, or if the ear-muffs were of too sheer a material, then Hans could hear and answer the questions which for human ears were inaudible. He demonstrated all this by means of experiments and of 20 tests of the first kind, in which auditory sensations were supposedly eliminated, 95% of the responses were incorrect (Hans would always tap too great a number) ; whereas of 28 tests of the second kind, not a single answer was wrong, just as had been predicted. Now I have repeated both kinds of tests, but have always found some correct responses in those cases in which the horse, supposedly, was unable to hear, a thing which greatly astonished Mr. von Osten. In fact, the responses of the horse were quite as correct when I did not even whisper the question inwardly. It was quite clear that putting the question in any form whatever was wholly unnecessary. Mr. von Osten's demonstrations to the contrary, which were based upon erroneous physical principles, are to be explained as cases of vivid autosuggestions, (but of this, more in Chapter V). After all this experimentation, it was manifest that the cue was not given to the horse while the question was being put ; it occurred, therefore, at some time during the process of tapping. But by means of which sense organ was it received by the horse?

We began by examining the sense of vision, and in the following manner. Blinders were applied, and it is worthy of mention that Hans made no attempt to resist. The questioner stood to the right of the horse, so that the animal knew him to be present and could hear, but not see him. Hans was requested to tap a certain number. Then the experimenter would step forward into the horse's field of vision and would put the same problem again. Since, in the tests of the first kind, Hans would always make the most strenuous efforts to get a view of the questioner, and since he would rave and tear at the lines whenever the attempt was made to tie him,—a thing which he had never done hitherto,—it was impossible to determine in some cases whether or not he had seen the questioner during the process of tapping. I am using, therefore, in the following exposition, besides the two categories of "not seen" and "seen", a third which I have called "undecided". A total of 102 tests were made in which large blinders were used. In 35 of these, the experimenter certainly was "not seen" in 56 cases he was "seen" and the remaining 11 are "undecided". Under the first of these categories 6% of Hans's answers were correct (i. e. only two), under the second head 89% were correct and under the third 18% were right. In other words, the horse was at a loss the moment he was prevented from seeing the questioner; whereas his responses were nearly always correct when the experimenter was in sight, certain proof that the horse's failures are to be attributed to the elimination of visual stimuli and not to the general inconvenience occasioned by the blinders. It is evident therefore, that the horse required certain visual stimuli or signs in order to make a correct response.*

* Throughout this treatise I am using the word "sign," or "signal," whereas all other writers who have touched upon the Hans-problem, have always spoken of "aids." Following von Sanden,[4] however, I would distinguish clearly between the two. I would designate as aids all immediate stimulations of the horse's body (i. e. by means of contact), which have been designed with reference to the animal's physiological movement-mechanism in such a way that they truly 'aid' him in the production of the required movements. I would regard as signs on the other hand, all stimulations (whether mediate or immediate) which are selected without especial regard to the anatomy or physiology

Such unequivocal results, however, were only obtained after we had provided blinders of sufficient size (15 × 15 centimeters). Mr. von Osten believing that the horse would not suffer these to be applied, had at first proposed other measures. He held a slate before his face. Some of the horse's responses were right, others wrong. The tests were repeated and were successful as long as I, myself, held the slate before my face, but not a single one of the responses was correct when another would attempt to hold the slate before me. Mr. von Osten then brought forth a kind of bolster which he fastened on the right side of the horse's face,—the side which was turned toward the questioner. But this also gave uncertain results. Finally he agreed to apply blinders. But these were much too small and projected at a great angle from the head (Mr. von Osten had cut the straps, for he thought they worried the animal). The result was that only the posterior part of the horse's normal field of vision was obstructed. Therefore, one could never be quite sure whether Hans, who—it will be borne in mind—made every attempt to see the questioner, had not perhaps after all been able to peer over the edge of the blinder. The number of " undecided " tests, therefore, became very great. Of 108 tests, only 25 could be placed in the

---

of the horse, and bear no inseparable relation to the thing to be done but are associated with it at the will of the trainer. The rider's use of reins, and control by means of leg-pressure and manner of sitting in the saddle, and the driver's use of the lines,—— all these, then are aids. A simple pull at the reins, however, is not an aid, but a sign. The whip may be used for giving signs as well as aids, —— the latter, when it does the work of the spur or of the pressure with the knees, as is the case with ladies' riding-horses and in lunging. All calls and all movements of the hand or head merely, on the part of the trainer, are to be regarded as signs.

category of " not seen ", 44 in the " seen ", and 39, i. e.,
a third of the total, in the " undecided." The percentage
of correct answers for these three categories were, respectively : 24%, 82% and 72%. Here we have once more
approximately the same ratio between the categories of
" seen " and " not seen " as in the case of the tests with
the smaller blinders. If we were to count the cases
which we had put under the head of " undecided," in the
same category as those in which vision had been excluded—as Mr. von Osten had done—then one would
have been led to the conclusion that the horse did not
need visual signs. Several observers had thus been led
astray: e. g., General Zobel writes in the " National-
Zeitung " (Aug. 28, 1904), that upon request Mr. von
Osten had covered Hans's right eye " by means of some
sort of blinder, so that he was unable to see his instructor ", and that Hans did not fail to respond correctly. We evidently have here to do with the unreliable
bolster mentioned above. Furthermore, Mr. Schillings
made a number of tests with the small blinders, in which
50% of the answers were correct, and probably in the
same manner were obtained the results published in one
of the daily papers (the " Berliner Tageblatt ", Dec. 12,
1904), several days after the publication of the December
report, and reading as follows: " Tests have been made
upon Hans with blinders over his eyes and it is to be
noted that, in spite of these, he still responds correctly."
Mention is also made of the experiments noted in Supplement III (page 257), in which Mr. von Osten hid behind the questioner and merely encouraged the animal
by occasional exhortations, but it is not possible to say
with any degree of certainty in how far he was really
hidden from the horse's view.

I would add that the horse—in so far as it was at all possible to decide—never looked at the persons or the objects which he was to count, or at the words which he was to read, yet he nevertheless gave the proper responses. But he would always make the most strenuous efforts to see the questioner. (See page 43). I would furthermore add that several experiments, in which Mr. von Osten and the horse were separated from each other by means of the canvas tent, failed completely, and that, on the other hand, all tests were successful in which the questioner was present in the feed-room and the door between this and the horse's stall was opened wide enough for him to be seen by the horse. I would also mention that toward evening the responses became less and less accurate. The conclusion that visual stimuli were here operative cannot be gainsaid.

It was possible, to be sure, that other senses might also be involved, but it was certain that auditory sensations did not enter it. This is shown by the fact that one might remain just as silent while the horse was tapping his answer as during the putting of the question and yet obtain a correct response. Hans, furthermore, could scarcely be distracted by auditory stimulations. If either the experimenter or anyone else present sought, at a given moment, to interrupt him by such calls as "Halt", "Wrong", etc., while he was going through the process of tapping, they very seldom succeeded in their attempt. Even though such interruption did succeed in seven out of the twenty-one cases in which it was tried, the assumption is well grounded that the success was due entirely or almost entirely to minimal movements involuntarily executed by those attempting the interruption. It is to such minimal movements that the horse, as we shall see later, promptly reacted. When the experimenter (Pfungst), himself, made the interjections, which certainly should have been more effective, we found that the horse was actually disturbed in only two of the fourteen cases; and finally in ten consecutive cases of attempted interruption not a single one was successful. There was almost a complete absence of any ear movements on the part of the horse, a fact in which I have been borne out by Mr. Henry Suermondt, the distinguished horseback rider. Indeed, I cannot recall that Hans ever turned his ears toward me, a fact which is strikingly curious in the case of a horse so attentive and so spirited in temper.

Finally, I might also mention that the breathing of the experimenter in no wise influenced the outcome of the experiment. Whether he held his breath or breathed on the leg or body of the horse, made no difference.

Investigations of the other senses became needless, for I had, in the meantime, succeeded in discovering the essential and effective signs in the course of my observations of Mr. von Osten. These signs are minimal movements of the head on the part of the experimenter. As soon as the experimenter had given a problem to the horse, he, involuntarily, bent his head and trunk slightly forward and the horse would then put the right foot forward and begin to tap, without, however, returning it each time to its original position. As soon as the desired number of taps was given, the questioner would make a slight upward jerk of the head. Thereupon the horse would immediately swing his foot in a wide circle, bringing it back to its original position. (This movement, which in the following exposition we shall designate as "the back step", was never included in the count.)

Now after Hans had ceased tapping, the questioner would raise his head and trunk to their normal position. This second, far coarser movement was not the signal for the back-step, but always followed it. But whenever this second movement was omitted, Hans, who had already brought back his foot to the original position and had thereby put it out of commission, as it were, would give one more tap with his left foot.

If it was true that these movements of the questioner guided the horse in his tapping, then the following must be shown: First, that the same movements were observed in Mr. von Osten in every case of successful response; secondly, that they recurred in the same order or with only slight individual changes in the case of all who were able to obtain successful responses from the horse, and that they were absent or occurred at the wrong time in all cases of unsuccessful response. Furthermore, it was observed that it was possible to bring about unsuccessful reactions on the part of the horse as soon as the movements were voluntarily suppressed, and conversely, that by voluntarily giving the necessary signs the horse might be made to respond at pleasure; so that anyone who possessed the knowledge of the proper signs could thereby gain control over the process of response on the part of the horse. These requirements have all been fulfilled, as we shall see in the following pages.

With regard to the regular recurrence of the movements noticed in the case of Mr. von Osten, I was, after some practice, able to note carefully their peculiar characteristics. This was rather difficult, not only on account of their extreme minuteness, but also because that very vivacious gentleman made sundry accompanying move-

ments and was constantly moving back and forth.   To
abstract from these the essential and really effective
movements was truly difficult.   It was much easier to
observe these movements in the case of Mr. Schillings,
probably on account of the fewer accompanying movements and perhaps on account of their greater distinct-
ness.   Usually he would raise the entire trunk a trifle, so
that the movements could be noticed from behind.   Besides these, I had an opportunity to observe the Count
zu Castell, Mr. Hahn and the Count Matuschka.   All
three made the same movements, though somewhat more
minutely than Mr. Schillings, yet none was as slight as
those of Mr. von Osten.*   I further noticed that Count
Matuschka and Mr. Schillings often showed a tendency
to accompany every tap of the horse with a slight nod
of the head, the last being accompanied by a more pronounced nod and then followed by the upward jerk of the
head, in other words, they beat time with the horse.   In
the case of the last three mentioned, for whom the horse
responded far less effectively than for Mr. von Osten or
Mr. Schillings, belated or precipitate jerks would frequently occur.   This was found to be true in the case of
all other persons who had failed to elicit adequate re-

* During the tests Mr. von Osten nearly always wore a slouch hat
with a wide rim.   The rim, of course, always moved with the head, and
made the movements appear on a larger scale, (in the ratio of about
3 : 2, as I was able to ascertain later by graphic methods).   But observation was successful, even at a distance of a meter and a half, when he
worked with head uncovered.   And even if head and forehead were
covered entirely, it was still possible to note the movements by watching the eye-brows.   When Mr. Schillings and the rest of us worked
with the horse, we either went bare-headed or wore only a very small
cap.

sponses from the horse. Often, in both cases, a complete absence of any kind of minimal movement had been noted. The accuracy of these observations in the case of Mr. von Osten is attested by Mr. Stumpf and Mr. von Hornbostel, and by these same gentlemen and Prof. F. Schumann in the case of Mr. Schillings and myself. They also found these movements to be most minute in the case of Mr. von Osten. In my case also they pronounced them " minimal, and often quite imperceptible ". All other persons who have seen me work with the horse, but who were not familiar with the nature of these movements, never perceived them, no matter how closely they observed me.

Since the doubt was expressed that these movements did not precede but followed closely upon the back-step of the horse (i. e., that an error with regard to the time-element was involved), it became important that time measurements be taken. This was done in the following manner: The questioner asked the horse to tap numbers from 5 to 20, seldom higher. He purposely refrained from pronouncing the number, but recorded it after each test had been completed. This was a matter of indifference to the horse (see page 42), and had the advantage that the measurement was not influenced by knowledge on the part of the time-keeper. Two observers were required, one watching the horse, the other the questioner. Both observers had fifth-second stop-watches. The larger face of this watch shows the fifth-second and a hand on the smaller face indicates the minute. By pressing upon the stem the watch may be set in motion at any moment desired, and by pressing it once more it may be instantly stopped, and the time elasping between the setting in motion and the stopping may be read on the face. By pressing upon the stem a third time the hands are brought back to zero, and the watch is ready for another test. At a moment agreed upon beforehand— usually the third tap of the horse—both observers started their watches. Practice tests had shown that this could be done with all the accuracy necessary in this case. As soon as the observer of the questioner noticed the latter's head movement he stopped his watch, and as soon as the observer of the horse noticed the latter's back-step he stopped his watch. Since the movement of the horse's foot does not occur as a jerk, but is of greater extent than a jerk would be, it was agreed that the observer was to stop the watch as soon as he recognized the back-step as such, not when the foot was being raised from the ground, because it was not then evident whether the horse would bring it back to the original position or whether he was preparing to give another tap, nor when he had brought his foot completely back, but at the moment in which it was evident that the horse intended to make the back-step. Experimentation had shown that an agreement as to this moment was possible. A tap with the left foot, which might possibly follow upon the back-step, could be left out of account. The difference in time between the two watches would show the time between the head-jerk of the questioner and the back-step of the horse,* and if the back-step was indeed a reaction upon

* For the benefit of those who are familiar with reaction-time experiments of this kind, I would state the following: The reaction to the head-jerk, on account of the minuteness of the latter, was sensory throughout, and therefore all precipitate reactions are entirely wanting. The reaction to the back-step was, like the preceding one, a reaction

the head-jerk, then the watches would have to show a later time for the back-step than for the head-jerk.

Measurements of this kind were taken for Mr. von Osten, Mr. Schillings and myself. In the case of the first two it was taken without any knowledge on their part. They did not even know that they were being observed, having been told that the measurements were for the sake of determining the horse's rate. In my case, to be sure, the time could not be taken without my knowledge. I succeeded, however, in eliminating the effect of this knowledge on my part. (Cf. pages 88 and 145.) Since the results obtained in the case of Mr. Schillings quite agree with those obtained in my case, it is evident they may be considered as being of equal value.

With regard to the number of tests the following table may be referred to. The first vertical column gives the

to a visual cue. (Hans's tapping was almost quite inaudible). Both stop-watches were carefully regulated. In order to eliminate also the constant error which might possibly arise as a result of some difference in the functioning of their pressure-mechanism, the two watches were always exchanged in the different series of tests, by the observer of the man and the observer of the horse. The two time-measurements obtained by the two observers contained, of course, the reaction-times of the observers themselves. In order to equalize the constant error which thereby arose, it was arranged that each observer should react alternately now to the man, now to the horse. In order to be perfectly safe, the reaction-times of those concerned, (von Hornbostel, Pfungst, Schumann and Stumpf), were later determined in the laboratory by means of the carefully regulated Hipp chronoscope. Separate determinations were made of the reactions to the head-jerk and to an imitation of the horse's back-step. Then the time which one observer took to react upon a head-jerk, was compared with the reaction-times of the other observers to the back-step. Since the greatest difference which was found in this comparison, did not exceed one-tenth second, the results obtained in the courtyard required no correction.

name of the questioner, i. e. the person operating with the horse. The four other columns give the number of tests made upon each of these. The name of the person who made the observation in each series is indicated at the head of the column. It is unnecessary to give the name of the observer of the horse, for the only difficulty lay in the observation of the questioner. The numerals I and II indicate two series taken at different times.

Questioner.	v. H.		Pf.		Schu.		St.	
	I	II	I	II	I	II	I	II
v. Osten............	9	15	34	17	–	—	8	27
Schillings...........	–	—	19	17	6	16	–	—
Pfungst.............	6	13	—	—	–	—	9	—

We have omitted from this table several tests in which the observer of the questioner noticed no head jerks whatever, and therefore could not arrest his stop-watch, although the horse responded correctly. Four tests of this kind were made by Mr. von Hornbostel, two by Mr. Pfungst, two by Mr. Schumann and five by Mr. Stumpf. In the case of Mr. Pfungst the horse gave the unusually high number of fifty taps. The attention of the observer had been taxed too long and had failed him (two seconds is the most favorable time). The head-jerk of Mr. von Osten evidently occurred during a lapse in Mr. Pfungst's attention and therefore remained unnoticed.

		v. H.		Pf.		Schu.		St.	
Questioner.		I	II	I	II	I	II	I	II
V. Osten.	R.	44%	60%	62%	88%	—	—	0%	48%
	W.	56%	20%	12%	0%	—	—	100%	22%
Pfungst.	R.	100%	92%	—	—	—	—	100%	—
	W.	0%	0%	—	—	—	—	0%	—
Schillings.	R.	—	—	74%	100%	83%	100%	—	—
	W.	—	—	5%	0%	17%	0%	—	—

The results of the experiments are given in the second table. The general arrangement corresponds to that of the first table. Even though the absolute number of tests was small, yet for the sake of giving a better general view, all values are given in percentages. The tests in which the movement of the questioner had preceded that of the horse—as had been anticipated—are recorded under " R " (right); under " W " (wrong), we have recorded those cases in which the testimony of the stop-watches—contrary to our expectation—indicated that the reverse order prevailed. Finally, those cases which would complete the 100%, i. e. those in which the watches indicate simultaneity of the movements in question, are not recorded.

From this table we may note the following: The time-measurements for Mr. Schillings and Mr. Pfungst are quite in agreement and go to show that the order in time of the head movement of the questioner and the back-step of the horse was exactly what had been expected. The few contradictory cases which occur in Series I of the observations upon Mr. Schillings are to be accounted for by the fact that he was here for the first time the subject of observation, whereas the recorded time-measurements in the case of Mr. Pfungst had been preceded by a number of practice tests. The results of the measurements taken in the case of Mr. von Osten were far less satisfactory. Even if one were to allow a series containing barely more than 50% of "right" cases as sufficient proof of the correctness of our expectation regarding the order of the movements of the questioner and the horse, only three of the six series obtained with Mr. von Osten as subject, would satisfy this expectation. However, since four of the six series show a greater number of cases of simultaneity (their percentage may be easily deduced by referring to the per cent of "right" and "wrong" cases), the proposed method would give a distorted view, and therefore it appears that the more correct method would be to consider simply the numerical ratio of the "right" and "wrong" cases. Since, furthermore, Series II shows, in every case, a decided change which is similar for all observers (note especially Pfungst), there can be no doubt but that practice is here involved, and that Series II is to be regarded as the true standard. Throughout this series we find a preponderance of "right" cases. Therefore, the table unmistakably confirms the expected order in time. That there were more "wrong" cases with Mr. von Osten as subject than with the other questioners is to be explained by the fact that the decisive movements were far less easily observed in this case, than in that of the other questioners. (See page 49.) We expect that Series III would show the same results, or approximately the same results in the case of Mr. von Osten that it did for Mr. Pfungst and Mr. Schillings, but unfortunately he declined to act as subject. In the meantime, however, new and decisive proof presented itself which destroyed all possible doubt.

Before adverting to it, let us consider in a few words the reaction-time of the horse,—the time elapsing between the final sign of the questioner and the reaction of the horse (i. e., the back-step). Unfortunately this time cannot be directly determined. All that can be ascertained from our time-measurements, is the time intervening between the moment of the head-jerk and the moment in which the reaction of the horse is noted. (See page 51). This time averaged, for the 127 measurements, .45 seconds. If we stated the unavoidable error, (obtained on the basis of extended supplementary measurements which it is not necessary to consider here) as .15 seconds, and apply it to the value found above, we obtain .3 seconds as the probable reaction-time of the horse.*

That the tapping—as well as all other movements of the horse—was nothing other than a reaction upon certain visual stimuli, was proved beyond a doubt by the fact that the voluntary execution of the head-jerk and of other movements—which we will describe in more detail later on,—brought about all the proper responses on the part of the horse. Thus, artificial synthesis became the test of the correctness of analytical observation.

To elucidate; if the questioner retained the erect position he elicited no response from the horse, say what he

---

* See page 126 on the corresponding reaction-time in the case of man. Similar tests have been made in the case of animals in only one instance, and that for dogs, by E. W. Weyer.[5] But, as might have been expected, they did not yield any satisfactory results.

would. If, however, he stooped over slightly, Hans would immediately begin to tap, whether or not he had been asked a question. It seems almost ridiculous that this should never have been noticed before, but it is easily understood, for as soon as the questioner gave the problem he bent forward—be it ever so slightly—in order to observe the horse's foot the more closely, for the foot was the horse's organ of speech. Hans would invariably begin to tap when I stooped to jot down some note I wished to make. Even to lower the head a little was sufficient to elicit a response, even though the body itself

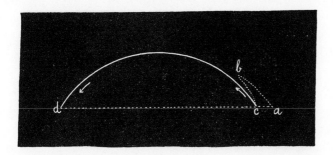

FIG. I.

might remain completely erect. Of thirty tests made in this position, twenty-nine were successful. Hans would continue to tap until the questioner again resumed a completely erect posture. If, for instance, I stooped forward after having told the horse to tap 13, and if I purposely remained in this position until I had counted 20, he would, without any hesitation, tap 20. If I asked him to add 3 and 4, but did not move until 14 was reached, he would tap 14. Twenty-six such tests gave similar results.

The reaction of the horse upon such a signal for stopping showed slight modifications according to the time which elapsed between the last tap and the signal for stopping. These modifications, which had hitherto been paraded as expressions of the horse's psychical power may be illustrated by the following schematic figures (Figures 1—4). In all of them the dotted line *c-d* represents the ground level; *d* shows where the horse's right forefoot was located before he began tapping; *a* and *c,* respectively, indicate the place to which the foot is lowered during the process of tapping. The unbroken line gives the direction of the back-step.

If Hans, having raised his foot from *a* to *b*—prepara-

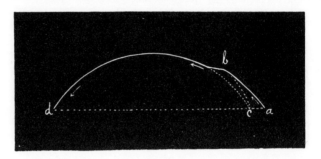

FIG. 2.

tory to tapping,—receives the signal at or just before the moment he lowers the foot, he immediately swings it in a wide circle from *c* back to its original position at *d,* (Fig. 1). As a matter of fact *a* and *c* coincide, but are juxtaposed in the diagram for the sake of schematic utility.) This was the usual form of the back-step.

If the signal for stopping is given a little after the last tap (Fig. 2), i. e., at the time that the foot is already being raised for another tap, then the back-step occurs as *a-b-d*. The horse thus gives, at the moment it receives the signal for stopping, a changed impulse to the moving foot. The curve, therefore, has a kink at b, and the back-step occurs with seeming hesitancy,—Hans appears not quite certain of his result.

If the signal be given somewhat later still (Fig. 3), i. e., when the foot is being lowered to complete a tap, Hans is still able to put on the brakes—as it were—and draw back his foot before it reaches the ground. The whole process gives the impression that the horse was just about to make a "mistake" of one unit, but at the last moment had bethought himself of the correct answer.

Finally, if the signal be deferred still longer, it becomes

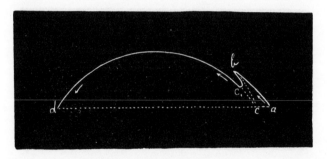

FIG. 3.

impossible to prevent the extra tap. The back-step again has the same form as in figure 1; Hans has made a "mistake" in his answer by one unit too many.

Conversely, if the head-jerk of the questioner occurs too soon; i. e., at the moment the horse has raised his foot for the final tap to the height b, (Fig. 4), then the tap is not completed,—but the foot, without touching the ground, makes the curve $b\ c_2\ d$, back to its original position. Hans has again made a "mistake" in his answer,—this time by one unit too few.

All these variations go to show one thing: Hans never

knows in advance which tap is to be the final one. These variations in his reactions occurred often without having been intended by the questioner. But to bring them about at will required skill, on account of the shortness of the time involved in the reaction.

Whenever the signal for stopping—which we have just discussed—was followed by the complete erection of the head and trunk, Hans would definitely cease tapping. If, however, the questioner failed to assume a completely erect position, or if he stooped forward ever so slightly, the horse would follow the back-step of the right foot

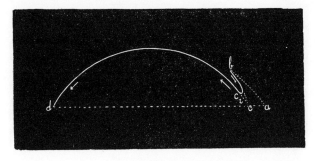

FIG. 4.

with an extra tap of the left foot. Besides occurring in tests in which Mr. von Osten assumed the rôle of questioner, this fact was also noted when the Count zu Castell and Mr. Schillings acted as subjects. Since the extra tap just mentioned was not given like the others with the right foot forward, but with the left foot upon the spot, it was possible for the horse to execute it with a greater show of energy. This simulated a high degree of mental certainty on the part of the horse, as if he wished to indicate that this was the correct solution of the problem and it would have to stand. In spite of all this, many errors would creep in. It was possible to prolong this extra tap and thus make it appear more dilatory. We need hardly add that henceforth it was within the power of the experimenter to have the tapping executed entirely with the right foot or with the final extra tap of the left foot. Hitherto the view had been current that this lay solely within the pleasure of the horse.

If the questioner still inclined forward, still remained in the bent posture after Hans had given the final tap with his left foot, the horse would immediately begin to tap once more with his right foot, which had, in the meantime, become ready for further action. If the head jerk was then made, Hans would bring his right foot back, give the extra tap with his left foot, then resume tapping with the right and thus continue until the questioner once more resumed the erect posture. Thus the horse on one occasion when I wished him to tap 100, gave—contrary to my desire—the following response; 39 with the right foot, 1 with the left, 24 with the right, 1 with the left, 35 with the right, and 1 with the left. Later it became possible for me to cause him to tap 1 right, 1 left, 1 right, 1 left, etc. I could even get him to tap exclusively with the left foot by standing at his left rather than at his right as had been customary with his questioners. These taps with the left foot were executed in a far less elegant fashion than those with the right foot, and with a great waste of energy. Hans had become a right-handed individual—as it were—as a result of long habit.

With regard to the distance at which the experimenter directed the horse, the following may be said: The usual distance was one-quarter to one-half meter. This holds for all tests hitherto described. Seventy tests which were made for the purpose of discovering the influence of change in distance showed that the reaction of the horse upon the customary signal of the head-jerk was accurate up to a distance of three and one-half meters. At a distance of three and one-half to four meters there suddenly occurred a fall of 60–70% in the number of correct responses. At a distance of four to four and one-half meters only one-third of the responses were correct, and at a distance beyond four and one-half meters there were no correct responses. The greater number of these tests were made in our presence by Mr. von Osten, who was under the impression that we were testing the accuracy of the horse's hearing, whereas we were really testing the accuracy of his perception of movements.

With regard to the different positions which the experimenter might assume with reference to the horse, the following may be noted: The normal position was to the right of the horse. If the experimenter stood immediately in front of Hans, the latter's reaction would be just as accurate, though he would always turn his head and make desperate efforts to see the questioner, even though he was held in short by the reins. When a position immediately behind the horse was taken—a somewhat dangerous proceeding, since Hans would at once begin to kick—no response could be obtained until he succeeded in turning far enough around to get the questioner within view. If he was restrained from turning completely around, he would at least turn his head,—and always to the right. One might even turn his back upon Hans during the tests, for the signal for stopping was not obtained from the face of the questioner, but from a movement of the head. The following incident will show to what extent the horse had become accustomed to seeing the questioner in a certain definite position. For a long

time I had been in the habit—without exception—of
standing close to the horse's shoulder. Mr. von Osten,
on the other hand, would stand farther back. When, on a
certain day, I assumed the latter position, the horse would
not suffer it, but would move backward until he had his
accustomed view of me.

Finally we sought to discover by what movements the
horse could be made to cease tapping. We discovered
that upward movements served as signals for stopping.
The raising of the head was the most effective, though
the raising of the eyebrows, or the dilation of the nostrils
—as in a sneer—seemed also to be efficacious. However,
it was impossible for me to discover whether or not these
latter movements were accompanied by some slight,
involuntary upward movement of the head. The upward
movement of the head was ineffective only when it did not
occur as a jerk, but was executed in a circuitous form,—
first upward and then back again. Such a movement was
occasionally observed in the case of Mr. von Osten. The
elevation of the arms or of the elbow nearest the horse, or
the elevation of the entire body was also effective. Even
if a placard, with which the experimenter tried to cover
his face, were raised at a given moment, the horse would
make the back-step. On the other hand, head movements
to the right and to the left or forward and back, in fine,
all horizontal movements, remained ineffective. We also
found that all hand movements, including the " wonderfully effective thrust of the hand into the pocket filled with
carrots ", brought no response. I might also change my
position and walk forward and then backward some distance behind the horse, but the back-step would only occur
in response to the characteristic stimulus. After what
has been said it is easy to understand how vain were Mr.

Schillings' attempts to disturb the horse and how naturally he might conclude that Hans was not influenced by visual signs. Mr. Schillings simply did not know which signs were effective.

While the horse could thus be interrupted in the process of tapping by movements which were executed at the level of the questioner's head, yet movements below this level had the opposite effect. If Hans showed that he was about to cease tapping before it was desired, it was possible to cause him to continue by simply bending forward a trifle more. The greater angle at which the questioner's trunk was now inclined caused the horse to increase the rate of tapping. The rule may be stated thus: The greater the angle at which the body inclined forward, the greater the horse's rate of tapping, and *vice versa*. It was noticeable that whenever Mr. von Osten asked for a relatively large number—in which case he always bent farther forward than in the case of smaller numbers—Hans would immediately begin to tap very swiftly. Not being entirely satisfied with these observations, the following more exact measurements were taken. I asked the horse to tap 20. From 1 to 10 I held my body at a certain constant angle, at 10 I suddenly bent farther forward and retained this posture until 20 had been reached. If there existed a relationship between the angle of inclination and the rate of tapping, then the time for the last ten taps ought to be less than for the first ten. Of 34 such tests 31 were sucessful. The following are two specimen series.

The first series consisted of ten tests of 15 taps each. In all cases my head was bent at an angle of 30° to the axis of the trunk, but I constantly changed the angle of inclination of the trunk. It was not possible to measure this angle accurately on account of the rapidity with which the whole test had to be made.   I was able, however, to differentiate between them with enough accuracy to designate the smallest angle (about 20°) as belonging to Grade I, and the greatest angle (about 100°) as belonging to Grade VII.   By fixing certain points in the environment, it was possible to get approximately the same angle repeatedly.   The time from the third to the thirteenth tap was, in all cases, taken by Prof. Stumpf by means of a stop-watch.   The tests were taken in the following order:

Grade of inclination:	I	VI	II	II	IV	V	VI	VII
Time for 10 taps:	5.2	4.6	5.0	5.0	4.8	4.8	4.6	4.4 sec.

From this series it will be seen that in the case of the same angle of inclination (II and VI were repeated and III was omitted) the same rate obtained in the tapping. In two other tests I constantly increased the angle of inclination during the 15 taps, and Hans gradually increased the rate of tapping accordingly.

In a second series I had the horse tap 14, five times. I myself took the time of the taps up to 7 by means of the stop-watch, while Prof. Stumpf took the time of the taps from 8 to 13.   At 8 I suddenly bent forward a little more and retained this position until tap 13.   The results were as follows:

Taps 2 to 7 (Pf.):	3.2	2.2–2.4	2.4	2.2–2.4	2.4 seconds.
" 8 to 13 (St.):	2.6	2.0	2.0	2.2	2.2 seconds.

Such good results, however, were possible only after a number of preliminary practice tests had been made. The experiment was especially difficult because the horse was often on the point of stopping in the midst of a test. This was probably due to some unintentional movement on my part.   In such cases I could induce him to continue tapping only by bending forward still more, but this effected also, as we have seen, an increase in his rate of tapping.   Such tests, of course, could not give unambiguous results.

The rate of tapping was quite independent of my rate of counting.   Thus, if I counted aloud rapidly, but bent forward only very slightly, the horse's tapping was slow and lagged behind my count.   If I counted slowly but bent far forward, Hans would tap rapidly and advance beyond my count.   Thus we see that his rate of tapping was in accordance with the degree of inclination of my body and never in accordance with the rate of my counting, i. e., it was quite independent of every sort of auditory stimulation.

Direct observation and a comparison of the records of the time Hans required in giving to his master responses involving small, medium and large numbers, with the records of the time which he required to respond to my questions when I bent only slightly, moderately or very far forward, proved that the increased rapidity in tapping in the case of large numbers, which many regarded as an evidence of high intelligence, (see page 20), was, as a matter of fact, brought about in the way described.   The two series (in each of which the time measured was for 10 taps) are quite in accord.   The horse did not tap faster because he had been given a large number by Mr. von Osten, but because the latter had bent farther forward.

From all this it readily appears why it was possible to cause Hans to increase his rate of tapping but not to decrease it.   To do the latter would involve a decrease in the angle of inclination of the body.   This would neces-

sitate the erection of the body.   As we have seen, this
was the signal to which Hans reacted by ceasing to tap.
And as a matter of fact we never knew the horse to
decrease his rate of tapping in the course of any single
test, except in the case of very large numbers, and then
it was probably due to fatigue.   Mr. von Osten insisted
that Hans often slowed down toward the end of a test,
" in order to obviate mistakes ", but all the tests in which
he tried to demonstrate this to us, were unsuccessful.   In
spite of all exhortation, Hans would tap either uniformly
or somewhat more rapidly as soon as his master—in all
probability unconsciously—bent somewhat lower.   Only
once was such a test successful.   Mr. von Osten—upon
our request—asked the horse to give a certain large
number.   In this instance the decrease in the rate of
tapping was due to fatigue and had nothing whatever
to do with the desire on the part of the horse to avoid
error.   Futhermore, Mr. Hahn, who had visited Hans
twenty times and had made careful notes of his observations, corroborated my statement when he said that he
himself never noted the decrease in rate mentioned.   Contrary statements may perhaps be due to the fact that the
tense state of expectancy on the part of the observer made
the interval between the last taps appear subjectively
somewhat longer.

So much for the technique of the tapping.   Now a
word about the numbers which Hans tapped.   (I refer
only to the results obtained in series which involved no
volitional control).   The number 1 was very difficult to
get.   Hans usually tapped 2 instead.   Thus even in the
case of Mr. von Osten he responded five times with 2,
and only in the sixth test did he react correctly.   As far
as other questioners were concerned, 1 was seldom ever

obtained, except in the case of Mr. Schillings and myself. The numbers 2, 3 and 4, on the other hand, were very easily obtained and, above all, 3 seldom failed. 3 seemed to be the horse's favorite number and was very frequently given instead of other numbers. Thus, one-sixth of all the horse's incorrect responses which were given to me were in terms of the number 3. The numbers 5 and 6 were a little more difficult to obtain and above 10 the difficulty increased rapidly. Indeed, I never saw Hans respond with a number exceeding 20 to any questioner, Mr. Schillings and Mr. von Osten excepted. I saw the nine vain attempts of Count zu Castell to get the number 15, and Count Matuschka's eight unsuccessful attempts to obtain the number 16 as a response. But even with Mr. von Osten and Mr. Schillings such failures were not infrequent. Thus, Mr. von Osten tried five consecutive times to obtain the number 24. I myself did not fare any better at first. But the following table shows what practice can do. If we compare the percentage of correct responses (involving the numbers 1 to 7—for which alone I have sufficient material, viz., 80 to 100 cases), obtained in the first half of our tests, with that of the second half, we get the following:

For number:	1	2	3	4	5	6	7
In first half of tests:	49,	92,	89,	86,	74,	62,	53%
" second " " :	92,	95,	92,	98,	97,	86,	96%

From this we see how hard it was at first to get the number 1 and that failure was as frequent as success, and how much easier it was on the other hand to get the numbers 2 and 3 (and which, therefore, do not show any great improvement in the second half of the tests). Beyond the 3 the percentage of correct responses decreased and the number 7 stood at the same level as the number 1. In the second half of the tests, all these differences disappeared and errors were infrequent and seldom exceeded + 1 or — 1. These results of practice are not to be accredited to the horse, but to the experimenter, who was at first quite unskilled. This difference in results does not appear in the case of Mr. von Osten, for his initial practice had been had many years previous. The values obtained in his case were very constant throughout our experimentation and generally showed something like 90% of correct responses. To be sure, in his case also, the number 1 was somewhat unfavorable, (79% were correct responses). But the percentages obtained in his case showed no improvement whatever throughout our experimentation. We need scarcely add that with the voluntary control of the giving of the signs, in the case at least of such small numbers as are here discussed, no errors, whatever, occurred.

We have discussed the influence of the experimenter, i. e., the one who asked the horse to tap; now let us consider the influence of others present upon the horse.

As a general rule, other persons had no effect upon the horse's responses. This appears from the failure of nearly all tests in which all of those present—with the exception of the questioner himself—knew the number which the horse was to tap. Even when the others concentrated their whole attention upon the number, it profited little as a close analysis of the 136 cases, which belong under this head in our records, go to prove. Thus, in the presence of a group of twenty interested persons—during the absence of Mr. von Osten—twenty-one problems were given to the horse, the solutions of which were known to everyone but myself, the questioner. Result: only two correct responses. Only when there was among the spectators someone to whom the horse was accustomed to respond or one from whom he regularly received his food, would such an influence be effective.*   But such cases

* Mr. Schillings, however, did succeed in making a number of tests with the co-operation of others who had never before worked with the horse. These tests wcre made under the following conditions : The horse was standing in his stall, when Mr. Schillings and another gentleman approached him. There was no one else present. Mr. Schillings, who tried to remain as passive inwardly, as possible, asked his partner to think consecutively of different numbers between one and 20, which thus were known to him alone. Hans was then commanded by Mr. Schillings to tap the numbers, which he did, to the great astonishment of the men, and especially of Mr. Schillings. In like manner Mr. Sander, a staff physician in the marine, received--so he writes me—three correct responses to four questions which he put to the horse. It happened also in the case of two scientific men and finally, too, in my own case, when I first came in contact with the horse, (see page 88). The horse's reaction was brought about in the same way in every one of these instances. Mr. Schillings, in bending forward slightly, thereby started the horse a-tapping, and his companion—just as innocently—interrupted the process by means of a movement of his head, when the right number of taps was reached.

I later tried similar experiments together with Mr. Hahn. I was aware of the answer to the riddle at the time, but he was not. Mr. Hahn stepped in front of the horse and thought intently of certain numbers. I did the questioning, that is, I got the horse to tap. In twelve tests Hans responded correctly in only two instances. In the ten others he always tapped beyond the number Mr. Hahn had in mind, e.g., 21 instead of 2, and was evidently awaiting a movement on my part. When we exchanged rôles, Mr. Hahn doing the questioning and I doing the " thinking," the horse would not respond at all, although as a rule Mr. Hahn had been fairly successful in working with him alone. I had gradually gained so much influence over the horse, that he would scarcely attend to any one else when I was about—Mr. von Osten hardly excepted.

In this connection I would prefer to avoid the term " rapport," which may rise in the minds of many, since it has been used so much in connection with the phenomena of hypnotism, for I would not obscure a fact that is clear by giving it a name that is vague.

were few.   The most important were the following:
I at one time whispered a number to Hans (on the occasion of the tests mentioned on page 37), and Mr. von
Osten asked for it the moment I stepped aside.   Hans
answered incorrectly even though I stood close beside
Mr. von Osten; I did not, however, think intently of the
number.   As soon as I concentrated my attention upon
the number he promptly responded correctly.   Further
cases are those mentioned on page 38, in which the
keeper of the horse unintentionally aided in giving four
dates which were unknown to all others present, including
the questioner.   This single instance shows the necessity
of the rule that during tests in which the method is that
of procedure without knowledge the solutions should be
known to no one of those present.   Finally the tests made
by the September-Commission and reported in Supplement III (page 255) may possibly belong under this head.
Since they were not followed out any further, I am unable
to render a definite judgment upon them.   In most of
these tests the question itself, as put by Mr. von Osten,
was not adequately answered, but curiously enough, however, the number which had been given to Hans in von
Osten's absence and which formed the initial number of
some mathematical operation, was tapped correctly.   This
may possibly be explained by the assumption that this
initial number had been retained in the memory of some
of those present, (see page 149, on the "perseverative
tendency"), and that the horse, since he had been working
with some of them, responded to one of those present.
Chance may have played some part also.

If the questioner knew the number of taps desired,
(which was not the case with the tests hitherto discussed),
then the environment had still less influence upon the

horse—except that it caused occasional interruption.   The
horse's responses, therefore, did not tend to become more
successful just because a number of persons were
simultaneously concentrating upon the result desired.
This was proven by the experiments which we repeatedly
made for this purpose.   Only one person at a time had
any influence upon Hans.   If two questioners tried to influence the horse at the same time,—other conditions being
the same,—success would be for the one who had the
greater control over the animal when working alone with
him.   Prof. Stumpf and I made the following experiment.
Both of us stood to the right of the horse, each thinking
of a number.   In ten such tests Hans always tapped my
number.   When Stumpf concentrated upon 5 and I upon
8, the horse responded with 8, i. e., the larger number.
When Stumpf had 7 in mind, and I had 4, the response
would be 4, i. e., the smaller number.   When Stumpf
thought of number 6, and I had fixed upon none, Hans
tapped 35.   He was evidently awaiting my signal.   When
I went away Stumpf again demanded the number 6, and
the horse responded properly.   When I returned, Stumpf's
attempts again failed.   On another occasion Count
Matuschka put a number of questions, while Mr. von
Osten stood behind him.   All of the horse's responses
were correct, even the one answering the question:
"How much is 7 times 7?", which was difficult on
account of the great number of taps required.   I was
able to note from the direction of the horse's eyes that he
was attending only to his master and not to the Count.
On still another occasion Mr. Grabow sang two tones—
the second being the fourth of the first—and asked Hans:
"How many intervals lie between?"   I was standing
erect before the horse, and was thinking intently of the

number 2, but without giving any voluntary sign of any sort. Hans tapped 2, whereupon Mr. Grabow put a number of similar questions; but I no longer thought of the answers, and all of Hans's responses went wrong.

Although Hans was not influenced by others so long as a suitable experimenter was present, yet he might be disturbed and under certain conditions might be led to make the back-step in response to certain movements in his environment. The person to whom he responded would have to be close to the experimenter and would necessarily have to execute a movement greater in extent than the experimenter's. In such instances the raising of the head, arm or trunk, was a sufficient stimulus. Thus we made the following two series of tests. Mr. Stumpf stood with trunk bent forward before the horse, and at a moment decided upon beforehand, assumed an erect position. I myself stood beside Hans and asked him to tap. When I stood at the horse's neck, then Mr. Stumpf's interruption was effective. When I stood at the horse's flank, the interruption effected only a seeming hesitation, and when I moved still farther back, the horse continued to tap despite any attempted disturbance. In the second series the questioner remained constantly at the right shoulder of the horse, while the one who attempted to distract him, changed positions. When the latter stood to the right immediately in front of or beside the questioner, the distrubance was effective in 10 out of 13 cases. But when he stood back of, and to the right of, the questioner, the attempts at disturbance were seldom successful. If he chose a place before and to the left of the horse, there was hardly any distraction (in 4 cases only, out of 13), and if he stood to the left and behind the animal, he exerted no influence whatever. Hans manifestly turned his attention, almost exclusively, to the side at which the questioner stood.

That knowledge of this *modus operandi* made it possible for those persons to get responses from the horse, who hitherto had been unsuccessful, is shown in the case of Mr. Stumpf when he began to control his movements voluntarily on the basis of observations which had been made.

II. *Problems which Hans solved by movements of the head.*

We are here concerned with the horse's head movements upward, downward, to the right and to the left, and also with nodding and shaking of the head to signify " yes " and " no ". We soon discovered that these experiments, also, were successful without an oral statement of the problem,—in other words, the auditory stimulus was quite superfluous. The tests with the blinders showed that Hans was lost as soon as his questioner was out of his view, but responded adequately the moment the questioner was in sight. Hans, therefore, had established no idea of any sort in connection with the terms " up ", " down ", etc., but in these cases, likewise, he reacted in response to certain visual stimuli. The nature of these stimuli I discovered at first in my observations of Mr. von Osten and also of myself, when working with the horse.

Above all things it was necessary that the questioner, during these tests, should stand perfectly erect. If he stooped ever so slightly, the test was unsuccessful. If he carefully refrained from any movement whatsoever, and looking straight before him asked the horse, " Which direction is right?" or "Which way is upward?", Hans would execute all sorts of head movements without rhyme or reason. It was evident that he noted that a head movement of some kind was expected of him, but did not know the particular one that was wanted. But if the questioner now raised his head, Hans would begin to nod and would continue doing so until the questioner lowered his head. This reaction was interpreted as signifying "yes". Mr. von Osten had always asked Hans before each of the more difficult tests whether he had comprehended the meaning of the problem, and was reassured only upon seeing the horse's affirmative response. But contrary to Mr. von Osten's expectation, Hans also responded in this manner after a pair of ear-caps had been drawn over his ears. In the case of the tests described at the beginning of the chapter, in which the method was that of "procedure without knowledge", Mr. von Osten had always insisted that we await Hans's nod of comprehension before proceeding. We complied; Hans nodded and— regularly disgraced himself!

When the questioner raised his head somewhat higher than normal, Hans would throw his own upward, which was supposed to signify "upward". A lowering of the head on the part of the questioner was followed by a lowering on the part of Hans, which was his form of response for "down". For some time I was in a quandary as to the difference between the questioner's signal for this latter response and the one which was the signal for the horse to begin tapping, although I had often given both kinds unwittingly. Further experiments showed that Hans responded with a nod of the head whenever the questioner, while bending forward, chanced to stand in front of, or to the side of the horse's head, but that he would begin to tap in response to the same signal, as soon as the experimenter stood farther back. The difference in the two signals, therefore, was very slight, and I repeatedly noted that instead of tapping, as he had been requested, Hans would respond to the Count zu Castell's and Mr. Schillings' questions by a nod of the head.

If, while standing in the customary position to the right of and facing the horse, the questioner would turn his head a little to the right—a movement which, when seen from the horse's position, would appear to be to the left,—Hans would turn his head to his left. But if on the other hand the questioner would turn slightly to the left,—i. e. seen from the horse's position, to the right,— then Hans would turn his head to his right. And finally, whenever the questioner turned his head first to the right, then to the left, Hans would respond by turning first to his left, then to his right. This, according to Mr. von Osten, signified " zero " or " no ". Since this movement could not be executed by the experimenter while in a stooping position, it can now readily be seen why it was that Hans, instead of shaking his head, always began to tap whenever a placard with " O " upon it, was shown to him in the course of the experiments in which the method was procedure without knowledge on the part of the questioner. The latter expected the horse to tap, and therefore bent forward. Like all of the horse's other forms of response, this, too, was always unsuccessful whenever the questioner stepped behind the animal. Although Hans had always responded to Mr. von Osten and Mr. Schillings, and at first also to me, by means of the stereotyped movement of the head to the right and then to the left to signify " zero " or " no ", I later succeeded in controlling my signals so as to get the inverted order in the horse's response.   In the case of Mr. Schillings and of Mr. von Osten all of the movements just described were very minute, and long after the movements, which were effective stimuli for releasing the process of tapping, were recognized, it was still exceedingly difficult to discover them in these two gentlemen.   The signal for " zero " and " no " was relatively the most pronounced of the group in the case of Mr. von Osten, while with Mr. Schillings it was the least pronounced, in comparison with his very strong " jerk ".   Yet in both cases Hans responded wtih absolute certainty.

It is now readily conceivable how it was possible to make the horse respond to all sorts of foolish questions, both by involuntary signs—i. e., expressions following upon the bare imaging of the response expected,—as well as by means of controlled signs.   One could thus obtain consecutively the answers " yes " and " no " to the same question.   Or one might ask: " Hans, where is your head? ", and Hans would bend to the earth.   " And where are your legs? "   He would look at the skies.   Etc.

Let us examine for a moment the directives which the horse required for the various positions.   If one called him, while he was running about the courtyard, he paid no attention whatever, but if one beckoned to him, he came immediately.   A raising of the hand brought him to a standstill.   If one now stepped forward or pointed one's hand in that direction, he would step forward, or vice versa, he would step backward.   By means of minimal movements of the head, of the arm nearest the horse, or of the whole body, Hans could be induced to assume the position one desired, without touching him or speaking a word.   I noticed this quite early in the course of the investigation. Once, when intending to ask the horse to step backward to the right, I inadvertently said "Step backward to the left!", whereupon he stepped backward to the right. In spite of my verbal error, I had involuntarily given him the proper directives.

Finally we may note that Mr. von Osten had occasionally asked the horse to jump or to rear. The command in this case was: "Jump", or the question was: "What do the horses do in the circus?". Since these tests were just as effective when the command was given silently, it was an indication that these, too, depended upon visual stimuli. What was necessary to cause the horse to step backward and then jump forward was to step backward oneself, or make a slight movement of the hand in that direction. If one wished to make him rear, it might be effected by throwing the arm or head slightly upward.

III. Problems, which Hans solved by approaching the objects to be designated.

The method pursued in these tests was the following: From five to eight pieces of colored cloth $\frac{1}{2} \times \frac{1}{4}$ meters in size were arranged in changing series upon the ground, the interval between them being equal to the width of one piece, or else they were hung upon a string a man's height above the ground. This method was also employed when placards of like size with written symbols were used. The horse stood ten paces away and opposite the middle of the series, while Mr. von Osten stood at his right. Hans was asked to go and point out the cloth of a certain color or the placard with a certain word upon it. If the cloth lay upon the ground, Hans picked it up with his mouth and carried it to the questioner.   If the cloth, like the placards, hung from the cord, he approached, pointed it out with his nose and then backed up to his original position.   Before approaching the objects, Hans was required to indicate, by tapping, the number of the place in the series (counting from left to right), which the cloth or placard occupied.   Mr. von Osten never omitted this requirement.   Then the command " Go! " was given, and Hans obeyed.   (As a matter of fact, a slight directive movement of the head or hand was just as effective as the spoken command).

The following cases, chosen in a haphazard fashion, show that the horse's indication of the object's place in the series, by means of tapping, was by no means a guarantee that he would point it out correctly.   Five placards hung from the cord.   Mr. von Osten asked: " What is the position, counting from left to right, of the placard which has the word ' aber ' inscribed upon it? ". Hans answered: 3.   (It was indeed the middle placard.) Then he was commanded: " Go! ".   Thereupon Hans went straight to the fourth placard.   On another occasion Hans happened to drop a brown cloth upon a black one.   His master asked him: " In which place are there two cloths? ".   Hans responded correctly, " In the second place ".   To the question " Which of the two is the black one? " he also answered rightly: " The lower one ". Upon being asked to get it, he brought the white cloth.

The large number and the irregularities of the errors showed that there was no manner of intelligence involved in the pointing out process.   Thus during the two months of our experimentation Hans was asked twenty-five times by Mr. von Osten to bring the green cloth.   Only six times did he succeed in the first attempt, while in five instances he selected an orange-colored cloth, four times a blue, three times a white one.

The fact that the errors were equally distributed over the tests with the colored cloths and those with the placards is strong evidence that the horse's response involved no intellectual process, for if that were the case, then the responses in the tests with the placards would have been very much more difficult, for they would have involved the ability to read, whereas the tests with the colored cloths demanded only that a few names be remembered. Nevertheless, the horse was as unsuccessful in tests of one kind as he was in those of the other, —even when Mr. von Osten acted as questioner. (50% failures in 78 placard tests; 46% failures in 103 color tests.)

The fact that commands which were purposely enunciated poorly, or else not spoken at all, were executed with just as much accuracy as those given aloud, strengthened us in our supposition. On one occasion I placed a blank placard with the others. When I ordered him to approach *tabula rasa,* he invariably went to the right one. The following illustrates how he fulfilled quite nonsensical commands. A series of blue and green cloths lay upon the ground. Being asked where the black, the orange, and the yellow cloths lay, Hans shook his head energetically, i. e. they were not there. And yet, upon being asked to bring them in the order named, he regularly brought one of the blue ones.

All this goes to show that Hans did not know the names of the colors (to say nothing of the symbols on the placards). It was plain that here also, as in all the other cases, he was controlled by signs made by the questioner, the nature of which I soon discovered. Standing erect, Mr. von Osten always turned head and trunk in the direction of the cloth or placard desired. Hans, keeping his eye on his master, would proceed in that direction. Even after he had already started out, thanks to his large visual field one could control his direction by turning slightly more to the right or to the left. If, however, he had already arrived at the row of placards or cloths, this method ceased to be effective, for then he could no longer see the experimenter. It made no difference whether the cloths lay on the ground, or were suspended, like the placards.

The following fact justifies the conclusion that the bodily attitude of the questioner was the effective signal. The more numerous the cloths, or the nearer they were placed together, the more difficult one would expect it to be for the horse to select the one indicated by the experimenter. Such was indeed the case, for the number of errors increased with the number of cloths presented.

But no matter how many cloths there might be, or how closely they might be placed, it was always possible to indicate either end of the row, for in that case one had merely to turn to the extreme left or the extreme right, and might even turn beyond the row. Hans seldom failed in these cases, whereas he made many errors when cloths or placards within the series were wanted.

To turn from the nature and number of Hans's errors, to their distribution,—observation proved the hypothesis that the nearer two cloths lay together, the greater was the chance of their being mistaken one for the other. If we designate as "error 1" all those cases in which Hans went to cloth II instead of to cloth I, cloth III instead of cloth II, to V instead of IV, etc., and as "error 2" when he mistook III for I, IV for II, in fine, when-

ever he went two places too far to the right or left, and as
" error 3 " whenever he went three places too far to
either side of the cloth desired, we find the following
grouping of errors:

With Mr. von Osten, a total of 63 errors,:

73 % .... " error 1 "
21 % .... " error 2 "
 4 % .... " error 3 "
 1 % .... " error 4 "
 1 % .... " error 5 "

With Mr. Pfungst, a total of 64 errors,:

68 % .... " error 1 "
20 % .... " error 2 "
11 % .... " error 3 "
 1 % .... " error 4 "
 0 % .... " error 5 ".

The most frequently recurring error, therefore, was the
one in which the horse, instead of going to the cloth
desired, approached the one immediately adjacent.   On
page 79 I said that Hans's errors were without system,
but only in so far as it was impossible to explain them on
a basis of the colors which seemingly were mistaken one
for the other.   A part of a series in which Mr. von Osten
acted as questioner may serve as an illustration.   The
order given is that of the experimental series as it
occurred.   Five colored cloths were used.

Color of the cloth
asked for: blue,   brown, brown, brown, brown, brown, green, green.
           | | | | | | | |
brought: orange, orange, green, green, yellow, green, blue, orange.

Place of cloth
asked for: V   II   II   II   II   II   III   III
            | | | | | | | |
brought: IV   IV   III   III   I   III   V   IV

The interpretation of this series which it would be hard to explain by a reference to the colors which were mistaken, is simply this: Cloths lying near together were regularly mistaken on the part of the horse.

Experimental control of the questioner's movements decided the question. If the questioner at first indicated the proper direction and then turned about after the horse had already started forward, he was as a rule misled. When the questioner did not face the cloths at all, but turned away at right angles, or when he turned his back upon them, Hans was completely at sea. If, on the other hand, the cloths were arranged, not in a row, but in several heaps, so that one might turn to a particular heap, but could not indicate a particular cloth, then Hans would regularly go to the proper heap, but would always bring forth the wrong cloth. After much persuasion Mr. von Osten consented to make a series of these tests himself. Hans's failures were deplorable. He would take up first one cloth then another, turn again to the first, etc. We would mention, however, that this apparent searching was not done spontaneously, but in reponse to Mr. von Osten's calls, such as " See there! ", " The blue! ", etc. Every time Mr. von Osten called, Hans would drop the cloth he was holding in his mouth, or he would turn away from the one he was about to grasp, and would then try another one,

In addition to these visual signs, the horse received auditory signals in these tests, (as in all others in which he was required to bring objects). As soon as the questioner noticed that Hans was about to take up the wrong cloth, all that was necessary to make him correct his error was to give some sort of an exclamation, such as " Wrong! ", " Look, you! ", " Blue! ", etc. Hans would

pass on as long as the calling continued. If he was pick-
ing up, or about to pick up, a cloth when the exclamation
was made, he would go on to the next; but if, at the time
he was on his way to a certain cloth, he would change his
direction in response to the call. If he stood before one
of the pieces at the time, but had not lowered his head, he
would pass on to the next. In all this he would adhere
to a certain routine of procedure. If he was approaching
a series from the right, then a call would cause him to
turn to the left, if he was coming from the left, he would
turn to the right. If he had approached the row of
cloths near the center, he would turn, in response to the
questioner's calls, to the left,—seldom, very seldom, to the
right. Mr. von Osten did not seem to be able to control
the responses of the horse, entirely. As a rule, but not
always, one call sufficed to make Hans pass on to the next
cloth. If too many calls were given, he would often go
too far. Loud exclamations were superfluous.

These statements are not mere assertions, but are
founded upon the records of the results. The tests in
which calls were made show a larger percentage of correct
responses than do those without calls. Of a total of 103
tests with colored cloths, which Mr. von Osten performed
for us, only 37% brought forth successful responses on
the part of the horse when visual signs were the only
directives and when there were no directions by means
of calls, whereas the total percentage of successful responses was 54%, if we add to the above those in which
the vocal exclamations helped to bring about success.
The corresponding percentages for the total of 78 tests
with the placards were 23% and 50%. In a total of 110
color tests I myself obtained 31% correct responses under
the first head, and 56% under the second head. In a

total of 59 tests with placards I succeeded in getting 31% correct responses under the first head and 46% under the second head. We must note that without verbal admonition only one-third of the tests brought forth correct responses, whereas one-half succeeded when those in which calls were used, are added. Still, this is a relatively poor showing. In the most favorable series that Mr. von Osten ever obtained in our presence—and there was only one such—50% of the responses 'without admonition' were correct, and 90% when all the correct reactions, both with and without admonition, were taken into account.

Not all the places in the row required the same amount of assistance by means of calls. Those positions which needed the most help, were those which it was most difficult to indicate to the horse by the visual sign, i. e., the attitude of the questioner's body. We noted above (page 81) that the cloths at either end of the row were less difficult to point out than those nearer the middle. If our hypothesis holds true, we would expect that the end cloths would involve fewer auditory signals in the process of pointing out, and those within the row a greater number of such signs. By way of illustration, I will cite one series of tests in which Mr. von Osten was questioner, chosen not because it is most conformable to my hypothesis but because it is the longest (48 consecutive tests with five cloths) which I have. In the upper row I am placing the successful responses without auditory signs, in the lower those involving both auditory and visual signs.

Place of the cloth		:	I	II	III	IV	V
No. of sucessful responses.	visual signs only	:	5	2	1	2	4
	visual and auditory signs	:	5	5	8	5	5

We see that without verbal admonition the first and last places are most favorable for success, the second and fourth far less, and the middle least favorable. These differences disappear when admonitions are introduced, for all of the places then have the same number of correct responses with the exception of the middle, which now has even more than the others.

One more experiment which I made will close the discussion. The following colors were placed from right to left: orange, blue, red, yellow, black, green. I turned my back upon them, and therefore could guide the horse by verbal commands only. I asked him to bring the orange. Hans approached the yellow. I now called three times, allowing a short interval between the calls. At the first " Go! " he passed from the yellow to the red, at the second from the red to the blue, and at the third from the blue to the orange, which he then proceeded to pick up and bring to me. I had noted this same thing in Mr. von Osten's tests, although there, there were often other factors entering in. By exercising the utmost precision in facing the cloths, and by using, in addition, suitable oral signs, I succeeded in getting Hans to bring, successively, each one of the six cloths in the row, and without a single error,—and all this in the presence of Mr. Schillings who did not have the slightest notion of the secret of my success.

We need hardly say, in passing, that all that was true of the tests with colored cloths, was also true of the tests in which the placards were used. It was all the same to the horse whichever was placed before him.

We have thus tested all of the horse's supposed achievements. None of them stood the critical test. It would have been gratifying to have repeated some of the experiments and to have made Hans the object of further psychological investigations, but unfortunately he was no longer at my disposal after the publication of the report of the December-Commission.   Some may say that we have had almost enough of a good thing, but we must bear in mind that many of the tests which were carried out,— such as those in which the method was that of " procedure without knowledge ", those in which the ear-muffs were used, those in which distractions were introduced,—had previously been made by other persons (see pages 41f. 45, 63), and with other results, than ours.   A more thorough test, therefore, would have been doubly desirable.

CHAPTER III

THE AUTHOR'S INTROSPECTIONS

In the preceding chapter we asked: What is it that determines the horse's movements? Independent thinking, or external signs?—We found that it was solely external signs, which we described as certain postures and movements of the questioner. Beyond a doubt these necessary signs were given involuntarily by all the persons involved and without any knowledge on their part that they were giving any such signs. This is to be seen from their statements, which cannot be cavilled at, as well as from the fact that several of them even to-day still doubt the correctness of the explanation which we are here offering. I myself for some time made these involuntary movements quite unwittingly and even after I had discovered the nature of these movements and had thus become enabled to call forth at will all the various responses on the part of the horse, I still succeeded in giving the signs in the earlier naïve involuntary manner. It is not easy, to be sure, to eliminate at once the influence of knowledge and to focus attention with the greatest amount of concentration on the number desired, rather than upon the movement which leads to a successful reaction on the part of the horse. To some this may appear impossible, but those who are accustomed to do work in psychological experimentation, will not deny the possibility of such exclusive concentration upon certain ideas.

If we now ask: " What occurred in the mind of the questioners, while they were giving the signs? ", the answer can be found only by way of the process which in psychology is technically called " introspection ", i. e. observation of self. In the following we will give the most important results of this process of self-observation, which took place in the same period in which the observations recorded in the preceding chapter were made.

My first experiments were made while the horse was counting or solving arithmetical problems and were as follows: Mr. Schillings, who was alone with me in the horse's barn, asked me to think of several numbers, maintaining that the horse would be able to indicate them correctly upon being asked. He stood to the right of the horse, I stood erect and at the side of Mr. Schillings. There was no one else present. Somewhat skeptical in attitude, I concentrated my mind consecutively on five small numbers. Hans tapped one of them incorrectly, one correctly and three by one unit too many. At the time I considered these attempts as unsuccessful and credited some curious chance with the answers which were correct, or nearly so. This was a mistake, for often during the following days, and in the absence of Mr. von Osten, the horse would give correct answers. Others, of course, would be incorrect, and usually the mistakes would be by one unit,—so that I soon saw that even in the horse's errors there lay some system. It will be seen that Hans responded to me from the very beginning, undoubtedly because I had had the opportunity of watching Mr von Osten and Mr. Schillings and had thus patterned my behavior after theirs. I was not at first successful in getting the horse to respond correctly in the case of large numbers. For in order to get complete control over the horse, and, what was, as I later discovered, more to the point, control of myself, some practice was needed. But I was able to work with the horse quite successfully, while I was still in the dark as to my own behavior.

From the very beginning Hans responded as promptly to those questions which I articulated merely inwardly, as to those which were spoken aloud. That all formulation of the question was unnecessary, however, was shown by the following experiments. If, for example, I did not think of any particular number until after the horse had begun to tap, and then fixed upon 5, he would tap 5. If, however, I told him to count to 6, but gave no further thought to the command after he had begun tapping, I would get an entirely wrong response. It was easy to obtain any answer one wished to a question, simply by focussing consciousness, with a great degree of intensity, upon the answer desired. Thus Hans answered my question: " How many angles has a hexagon? ", first by 6, then 2, then 27, in accordance with the numbers that came into my mind. The animal always followed the ideas which were in the questioner's mind, and never his words, for it was with the former that the movements upon which the horse depended were bound up.

It was not enough, however, simply to imagine the number desired. It was furthermore necessary that the questioner be conscious of the moment when the horse reached that number. Larger numbers (above 6) were therefore, successful only when every single tap was inwardly counted to the end. The manner of counting was indifferent. Thus I counted 6 as follows: 1, 2, 3, 4, 5, 6, and later: 6, 5, 4, 3, 2, 1, and then again: 6, 6, 6, 6, 6, 6. Finally I used the Greek letters and also nonsense syllables. And in all cases I obtained six taps, the correct response. If, however, I simply counted the taps without knowing when the desired number was reached, the responses were always incorrect, e. g., I counted

For No. 10:	10, 10, 10	continuously,	Hans tapped	13,
" " 10:	1, 2, 3 to 10		" "	10,
" " 12:	12, 12, 12	continuously	" "	15,
" " 12:	1, 2, 3 to 12		" "	12.

In the case of smaller numbers, on the other hand, one often obtained correct results without counting. In this I am borne out by Mr. Schillings. It was merely necessary to image vividly the number 3, or 4, or even the name of a week-day or of a month without the number which would indicate it. In the last of these cases the number corresponding to the day or the month (e. g. 3 for Tuesday, 5 for May, etc.), though not consciously presented, still evidently lay at hand in the subconscious. To use a popular expression, I usually had a "feeling" when Hans had arrived at the right number.

It was furthermore found that it was not only necessary to count to, or to think of, the number desired, but that this must take place with a high degree of tension of expectancy—that is, a strong affective element must enter in. The state required for a successful response was not the mere passive expectation that the horse would tap the number demanded of him nor the wish that he might tap it, but rather the determination that he should do it. An inward "Thou shalt", as it were, was spoken to the horse. This affective state was registered in consciousness in terms of sensation of tension in the musculature of the head and neck, by intraorganic sensations, and finally by a steadily rising feeling of unpleasantness. When the final number was reached, the tension would suddenly be released, and a curious feeling of relaxation would ensue. I have made a series of tests to determine the most favorable degree of tension in expectation. It was possible to distinguish with certainty, three degrees of tension besides the state of utter relaxation,—all of which I measured by means of the differences in the sensations of tension. In cases of tension of the first degree (greatest concentration) the responses were usually correct, a few, however, were lacking by one unit. There was therefore in the latter instance a premature release of inner tension. In cases of tension of the second degree all answers were correct except a very few which were too great by one unit. In cases of tension of the third degree, many answers were wrong, and usually by several units too many. I wished to have the horse tap 10, with the lowest degree of concentration. He tapped 13, then in a repetition of the test, 12. I thereupon increased the tension, Hans then tapped 8. I decreased the tension once more, but so that it was somewhat greater than at first. Hans tapped 10 correctly. At another time I tried to have him tap the number 5, with a low degree of tension. He tapped 6. I intensified expectation and Hans tapped 4. I again decreased it, and he tapped 5, *comme il faut.* Apparently, therefore, the most favorable degree of tension was one between the first and second, —the latter being the least favorable. After some practice a lesser degree than was used in the beginning sufficed to evoke adequate reactions. The flow of nervous energy to the motor centers of the brain evidently became facilitated through practice. It will be easy to understand why the first days of experimentation caused intense headaches, which later never occurred.

Whenever, in the foregoing, we spoke of a certain degree of concentration which had to be attained, it is not to be understood that the same tension had to be maintained throughout the test, from the horse's first tap to his last. But rather, that it began with a low degree, and gradually increased as the final unit of the count was being approached. It may best be represented by a curve whose maximum represents that degree of tension which we have been discussing. The rise to this maximum which, when attained, was followed by a sudden fall, did not always occur in the same manner. Three types of curve may be distinguished, which were first discovered in purely empirical fashion, and later reproduced voluntarily for purposes of experimentation by diagramming before each test the intricate curve of the varying degrees which the intensity of concentration was to assume. The types may be described as follows:

I. Here the tension curve rises steadily from beginning to end. This type preponderates in the case of small numbers. Thus, when I asked the horse: " How much is 2 plus 4? ", the tension increased slowly with every tap from the moment I began counting, until the final tap was reached, when it was again relaxed. Externally this relaxation is noticeable as a slight jerk.

II. In this case the curve does not rise at an equal rate, but rather more slowly at the beginning and later undergoes a sudden increase, or the tension increases immediately at the beginning, remains constant for some time and then ascends to the maximum. This curve is the rule in the case of large numbers and evidently means economy of physical energy, for experience soon taught that a steady increase in tension from the very beginning soon brought it to a level which cannot be long maintained and usually leads to a premature relaxation. In the case of very large numbers the alternation of the slight and the sudden increase may be repeated several times, and at times it may even sink below a level which has already been attained, thus making a wave-like curve.

III. The third type of curve shows a sudden jump between two units at a certain point in its course. This may occur in the case of both small and large numbers but only when the highest or first degree of concentration is employed (see page 91). Such a jump frequently occurs in the transition from the tap preceding the last to the last one which is being eagerly expected. Relaxation—with the upward jerk and raising of the head— here occurs at the normal time; Hans taps to the end with his right foot. Oftener still the " jump " described occurs while passing over to the number just before the last. The goal seems within reach and the mental tension relaxes, and with it the physical tension,—the head gives a slight jerk and Hans makes the back-step. Since, however, another tap is still awaited with some degree of tenseness and, since complete erection of the head does not follow immediately upon the jerk of the head, the horse gives another tap with the left foot. Thereupon occurs the complete relaxation of attention, and the assumption of the erect posture on the part of the questioner. That this is psychologically the clue which leads to the final tap, will readily appear from the following remarkable fact: I was able to bring about at will either the back-step with the right foot, or the additional extra tap with the left foot by concentrating the mind either upon the last unit or upon the one just preceding it. In either case the movement which served as stimulus to the horse followed naturally upon concentration on the number. I could of course also control the response by direct voluntary control of the movements involved. Hans thus solved for me the same ten problems first with the back-step, then with the extra final tap.

Finally we will indicate the one true inner cause of the difficulty in getting the number 1 as a response. It is not easy to relax attention immediately after having just begun to concentrate. Relaxation, therefore, often occurs with a certain retardation, and the result is a belated jerk of the head.

Briefly, I would also mention a few of the more interesting introspective observations which were made in situations in which the horse responded with movements of the head for answers such as " yes " and " no ", " up " and " down ", etc. From the very beginning I put questions to Hans which would have to be answered by a shake of the head. It often happened that instead of indicating " o ", Hans would begin tapping some number. But the wonder of it was that, in many cases, he responded properly. I knew only that I inwardly pronounced the word " null " (zero), and that I looked expectantly at the horse's head. In the case of questions to which I expected the answer " yes " or " no ", I imagined myself enunciating the answer, i. e., I used motor imagery. The tests failed, the moment I employed only visual or auditory imagery, whereas, motor imagery was always effective in calling forth correct reactions.* When

---

* Thus it is possible to think of the word "no " in three different ways. I may get a visual image of the written or printed word, or the auditory image of the word as spoken by another person, or finally I might think of it in terms of images of the sensations of movement which would arise if I myself were to enunciate or write the word. And so, in like manner, I could think of any other word in terms of either visual or auditory or motor imagery. In all probability the

the proper response was "up" and "down" I would think of those directions in space, and likewise with "left" and "right" in which case also I would put myself in the horse's place.

While I was still ignorant of the nature of the necessary movements, the tests were successful only when I had put the question aloud or in a whisper, but never when I failed to enunciate, i. e., when I merely had the question in mind ("in idea"). But this also became possible after a little practice, although I could not then give an explanation for my success. Except in one instance, we could discern no difference between problems spoken and those merely conceived by Mr. von Osten who had had the advantage of long practice. But the one exception deserves mention. The old gentleman commissioned Hans, presumably without uttering a word, to step backward to the left. Hans thereupon responded by giving his entire repertoire, as follows: He moved his head to the right, then to the left. Then he leaped forward and repeated the same movement of the head. Hereupon he stepped backward and signified a "yes" by a movement of the head. He then lowered his head and made two leaps forward. After this performance Mr. von Osten repeated the same command aloud, and in every case Hans responded properly. Again the silent command was given and again the horse responded with the series of reactions described above, lowering his head

---

auditory and motor always occur together,[6] but still it is possible to make the one or the other predominate.

It appears that the imagery of most persons is a mixture of auditory-motor and visual elements, with a predominance of one or the other kind. Individuals who utilize almost exclusively the visual (as does the author, as a rule), are rare. But rarer still is the pronounced motor type.

leaping forward, etc. In this experiment, without exception, the spoken command evoked adequate reactions,—
the silent command, an incorrect response. Evidently
the impulse to movement was not so great with the mere
conceiving of " right ", " left ", etc., as when the words
were enunciated. It, therefore, required some practice
on my part before a sufficiently strong movement-impulse
became associated with the idea. All this is in no wise
at variance with the fact that tests involving counting and
computation were as successful when the problem was
given in silence, as when it was spoken. The signs for
tapping, viz.: inclination and erection of the head and
body, followed the question. The question therefore became superfluous. On the other hand the signs for head-
movements on the part of the horse, were given while the
question was being put. I ask, which way is " upward ",
and at the same time I look upward. In this case therefore the question itself is not entirely insignificant.—I experienced greater difficulty in getting Hans to respond
with the head-movement to the left. After much practice I was able to evoke this movement by means of
giving the command aloud, but never by means of the
" silent " command. Accidentally I hit upon a device by
means of which I attained this end also. I asked the horse
aloud " Which direction is left? ",—whereupon he reacted properly; then I immediately repeated the question
silently, and was successful every time. My mental attitude here was still the same as when I put the question
aloud. What sort of an attitude this was, I could not, of
course, have stated explicitly at the time. I could not,
therefore, awaken it at will,—and if I allowed but a
minute to elapse between the spoken and the silent question, the vivid after-effect (the so-called " primary mem-

ory image ") soon disappeared and the test was wholly unsuccessful. Practice, however, soon helped me to overcome this last difficulty also. I believe that my inability to evoke this specific reaction on the part of the horse, lay in the unfavorable position which I assumed, for it did not allow the horse to preceive my movements easily. For the same reason, Hans would at first indicate " no " and " zero " by turning to the right, seldom to the left.

As in the case of counting, a high degree of concentration was also necessary here, but with this difference, that here attention was directed to ideas present to the mind, (" yes ", " no ", etc.), whereas in the counting process attention was directed toward expected sensory impressions (i. e., the taps of the horse).

All that has been said thus far is readily understood psychologically. The following curious fact, however, is noteworthy. Hans used the head-movement to indicate two such different concepts as " zero " and " no "; it appeared therefore that in both cases he was receiving the same kind of directive. Observation proved that such was the case and the directive in question was none other than an imitation in miniature, or rather a movement anticipatory of the expected head-movement of the horse. Now, whereas the signs for " up ", " down ", " right ", and " left " were natural expressive movements which are normally associated with the corresponding concepts, this cannot be said to be true of " no ' and " zero ". My laboratory observations (see page 107) lead me to conclude that the movements, by means of which the concepts " no " and " zero " are naturally expressed, are quite different; and neither of these corresponds to the signs for " zero " and " no " which the questioner involuntarily gave to Hans. What was the genesis of these unnatural forms of expression? If we might assume that the questioner always had in mind the movement he awaited on the part of the horse, and never thought of " zero " or " no ", then the contradiction would solve itself. But I must deny decidedly that I ever thought of the movements of the horse's head, and Mr. Schillings, whom I questioned on this point, agreed with me in this, in so far as his own mental processes were concerned. I can see nothing for it but that in this instance the expressive movements normally connected with the concepts " zero " and " no " have been replaced by other forms, without the questioner becoming aware of it. That such displacements may occur, has been shown by the tests described on pages 107 to 112. That they did occur in this instance may be concluded from the following observation. In responding to me, as well as to Mr. Schillings, Hans always moved his head first to the left, then to the right, never in the opposite order. That this was *not* a peculiarity of the horse, but must be ascribed to the signs which were given him, is shown by the possibility of inverting the order under experimental control (page 77). Frequently Mr. Schillings and I had seen the horse respond to his master by means of such head-movements, and the order was always, without exception, the one mentioned. It must be assumed therefore that the horse's movement, which we so often noticed, made such an impression upon us, that afterwards it was regularly reproduced on our part quite unconsciously, so that Mr. Schillings never, and I only after a long time, became aware of the whole process.

In closing, just a word as to the discovery of our own movements. I soon noticed that every pronounced raising of the head or trunk brought about an interruption

in the horse's response. But only by observing the final
movement in the case of Mr. von Osten did I discover
that I, too, performed a slight erection of the head. Observation of others was less difficult than the observation
of one's own movements. As in the case of all other signs
given to the horse, these movements were so slight that
they were prone to escape notice even though one's whole
attention were concentrated upon their detection. I also
questioned whether in my attempts to disturb the horse by
means of loud calls, it were really the call or some simul-
taneous involuntary movement which was the true cause
of the interruption. The doubt was justified, for when
I finally learned to cry out vehemently without making
the slightest move, all my crying was in vain. Also it
had seemed to me at first as if I were able to induce the
horse to rear, not only by means of the proper sign or
movement, but also by a mere command, but I found
later that in every case there was always some movement,
were it ever so slight. Finally I tried to simulate voluntarily the oft-mentioned involuntary jerks of the head.
Although it is not very difficult to execute them at will
with almost the same minuteness as when they were performed involuntarily, I still did not succeed in getting a
series of such jerks of equal fineness throughout. In
spite of (and partly on account of) the most concentrated
attention, there would be from time to time a jerk of
somewhat greater extent and energy. As soon as the
movement had been executed, I was able to form a good
judgment as to its relative extent, but I was unable to
regulate the impulse beforehand.

With the following comment the chapter will be concluded. Introspections are necessarily subjective in character. If they are to possess general validity, they must

be borne out by evidence furnished by others—and this to a greater extent than is necessary for other forms of observation. It was hardly possible to get corroboration from the other persons who had worked with Hans, for, although some of them were excellent observers of external natural phenomena, few of them had had the necessary amount of practice in introspection. The necessary confirmation, however, was had in laboratory tests, which we shall presently describe.

CHAPTER IV

LABORATORY TESTS

THE tests which are to be briefly reported here, were begun in November, 1904, and were carried out at the Psychological Institute of the University of Berlin. The purpose was twofold: first, to discover whether the expressive movements noted in Mr. von Osten, Mr. Schillings, and others, were to be regarded as typical and to be found in the majority of individuals,—and secondly, to ascertain in how far the psychical processes which I had noted in my own case and which I believed to lie at bottom of these movements, were paralleled in, and confirmed by, the introspections of others. The effort was made to make the experimental conditions as nearly as possible like those under which the horse had worked. The affective atmosphere which colored the situations in which the horse took part, could not, of course, be transferred, but this was in some respects an advantage. One person undertook the rôle of questioner, another—myself —that of the horse. The experiments fall into three groups, corresponding to the types of the horse's reactions: 1, tests in counting and computation; 2, tests in space reactions; 3, tests in fetching or designating objects.

In the experiments in counting and computation, the questioner, standing at my right, thought with a high degree of concentration of some number (usually between 1 and 10, but sometimes also as high as 100), or of some simple problem in addition. Then I would begin to tap,—but in human fashion with my right hand, rather than with my foot—and continued until I believed that I had perceived a final signal. I thus tested, all in all, twenty-five persons, of every age and sex (including children of five and six years), differing also in nationality and occupation. None of them was aware of the purpose of the experiments. It could not escape them, to be sure, that they were being watched. It was also evident to them that the things noted were certain tensions and movements; but none of my subjects discovered what the particular phenomena were that I was looking for. Only in a few isolated instances did they report that they were conscious of any movements on their part. With the exception of two persons, they all made the same involuntary movements which were described in chapter II, the most important of which was the sudden slight upward jerk of the head when the final number was reached. It was at once evident that the direction of this jerk depended upon the position which one had asked the subject to assume at the beginning of the test, the direction changing whenever the position was changed. Thus, if the subject stood with head bowed— the body either being held erect or likewise bowed,—then release of tension would be expressed physically by an upward jerk. (Occasionally the entire trunk is slightly raised, so that it was possible to observe this physical reaction when standing behind the subject). If the subject had bent his head backward, the " psychological moment " was marked by a forward movement, (although under certain conditions the head was, in such a case, observed to bend still farther backward). If during the tests the head was bent slightly to the right, then the reaction was expressed in a movement toward the left, and *vice versa,* if it had been on the left, it was bent to the right. If the subject had been bending his head forward and to the right, he then raised it upward and to the left, etc. In all of these changes of position I noticed an intermediate posture which, to be sure, it was not always an easy matter to discover,—viz.: an upright position in which there was discernible no manner of head-movement or only a slight tremor. If the subject was lying on his back with his head supported, then there was noticeable a very slight movement to one side. In this same way a number of other positions were tested in order to discover for each the characteristic movement expressive of release of tension. It would therefore appear that the raising of the questioner's head, which served as the signal for stopping for Mr. von Osten's horse, was but one instance of a general law which may perhaps be stated thus: The release of muscular tension which occurs with the cessation of psychic tension, tends to bring about that position of the head (and body) which, at the time, represents the slightest amount of muscular strain.—These movements seldom were pronounced enough to be compared to motion through a distance of one millimeter, in a very few cases only did they attain to the magnitude of one or two millimeters. I failed to note them entirely, however, in only two individuals, two scientific men whose mode of thought was always the most abstract, and one of these was, in spite of repeated attempts, unable to elicit any response whatever on the part of the horse.

In the cases of the more suitable subjects I was able to indicate not only the number they had in mind, but also the divisions in which the number was thought, thus 12 as 5 and 5 and 2, or the same number as 2 and 5 and 5, and I was also able to determine the addends in the addition—i. e., whether the problem had been conceived as 3+2=5 or as 2+3=5. It frequently happened that in the beginning I would sometimes mistake these subdivisions, which were recognizable by the less pronounced jerks, for the final number. Thus I would often respond with 4 instead of 8, or 3 instead of 9, or with 3 when the problem was 3+2, just as Hans had so often done. In these tests, too, the difficulty of getting the number 1, as well as the larger numbers, came to light. Thus three times in succession 17 was indicated as 4, as 9, and as 17. But after some practice I was able to give numbers as high as 58 and 96. The frequency of the errors of one unit too many and of one unit too few is also noticeable in these tests.

We also found desirable corroboration, by trustworthy subjects, of the introspective observations of the author, which were reported in Chapter III, with regard to the significance of concentration and the curve of attention. It is hardly necessary to mention that no attempts were made to influence the subjects in their accounts by asking suggestive questions. The most valuable feature about these tests was that the mute horse had now been replaced, as it were, by an animal capable of speech, and that it was now possible to follow the same process both from within and from without. Two illustrations may be welcome. The one who took the part of the horse gave three taps and made the following entry: " At 3 I saw a slight upward jerk of the head on the part of the questioner ". The questioner however had thought of 4, and made the following note, without knowledge of the other's entry: " I was aware of extreme tension, so that it was impossible for me to get beyond 3 ". Or again, the 'horse', reacting to a movement on the part of the questioner, stopped at 3, but the latter, having intended to obtain 2, made the following entry: "I noted clearly that I ceased thinking of the number too late, and did not put on the brakes, as it were, until I had arrived at 3". We see that errors here were entirely the fault of the questioner, just as had been the case in the tests with Hans. (See page 151f.).

In a second group of experiments I asked a subject to fix his mind upon certain concepts, such as "up", or "down", "right" or "left", "yes" or "no", and others, in any order he pleased, but with the greatest possible degree of concentration. The subject each time had the choice of four or six concepts, and he was told to think of one of them at the signal "Now!". How he was to 'think' the concept was left entirely to him. He was also told to interpolate the series with a 'blank', that is, to think of nothing at all. Standing opposite the subject, I tried to guess at the mental content of the person's mind, on the basis of expressive movements. Sometimes I reacted by shaking or nodding the head, etc., just as Hans had done, but as a rule I was content to say the word which I thought the subject had in mind. With twelve subjects (a total of 350 tests) I made an average of 73% correct responses, and in the more favorable cases I attained even 90 to 100% correct responses. Very slight involuntary movements of the head and eyes, which showed but little individual variation, and always occurred when the subject began to fix upon the concept, were the signs which I used as cues. As in the case of the movements expressive of the release of tension, which I discussed above, these movements, too, occurred without the subject being aware of them, (except in those rare cases in which they had once or twice been especially pronounced). Indeed, it was very difficult and in some cases almost impossible for those persons whom I had initiated into the secret, to inhibit them voluntarily. "Up" and "down", "right" and "left", were expressed by movements of head or eye in those directions, "forward" by a forward movement of the head, "back" by a corresponding movement. "Yes" was accompanied by a slight nod of the head; "no" by two to four rapid turnings of the head to either side.* "Zero" was expressed by a movement of the head describing an oval in the air. Indeed, it was even possible to discover whether the subject had conceived of a printed or a written zero, for the characteristics of both were revealed in the head-movements. I was able later to verify this graphically. With Ch. as subject, I made 70% correct

---

* It was Charles Darwin [7] who first pointed out that the expressive movements (of the coarser sort) to be noted in nearly every race and people show a great, though by no means complete, similarity. The similarity is most pronounced in the shaking of the head to signify negation and nodding to denote affirmation. It will be noted that the former is essentially of the nature of a turning toward, and the latter a turning away.[8] These same movements have been reported in the case of the blind and deaf Laura Bridgman,[9] and we have been explicitly assured that they were a spontaneous development, and not acquired by imitation. For it is by imitation and never before the completion of the first year, that our children acquire these movements. On account of his unreliability, we can put but little stock in the statement of Garner,[10] a writer on the speech of monkeys, that these same gestures have been observed in the case of those animals. My experiments show that the same movements, greatly diminished in scope, as a rule accompany the mere thought of "yes," "no," etc. I cannot, however, regard the assertion as an established fact that every thought process whatsoever is connected with some form of muscular movement, as has been generalized by the French physiologist Féré,[11] and the American psychologist Wm. James.[12]

interpretations in a total of 20 tests; with von A. as subject, 72% in a total of 25 tests. And finally I was able to interpret the signs without any errors at all. It was not absolutely necessary to look directly at the subject's face. Even though I focussed a point quite to one side, so that the image of the subject's face would fall upon a peripheral portion of my retina, I still was able to make 89% correct interpretations in a total of 20 tests.—This is not astonishing after all, when we recall that the periphery of the retina possesses a relatively high sensitivity for movement impressions, although its chromatic sensitivity is very low.*

It was assumed, as indicated on page 99, that in the case of Mr. Schillings and myself the movements naturally expressive of " zero " and " no " had been displaced

---

* The productions of mind-readers, so-called, also, are based upon the perception of involuntary movements, insofar as they are not based upon pre-arranged schemes and trickery. But there we have to do principally with tactual perception, since the reader touches the hand of the subject and is guided by its tremor. Some of the expert mind-readers, however, conduct tests without touching the subject. They depend chiefly upon auditory impressions: the sound of footsteps,[13] involuntary whisperings [14] and the changes in the subject's respiration [15] and the murmuring of the spectators. To a less degree visual signs also are involved : posture and facial expression of the subject, and movements of eyes and lips.[16] Even the heat radiating from the person's body is supposed to have some influence.[17] And my own experience has taught me that surprising results may be obtained by the utilization of the movements described in the preceding chapter.

It may be that these truly microscopic movements also play some part in bringing about the success of some of the experiments in telepathy, so-called, (transference of thought from one person to another, ostensibly without any mediation of the senses known to us.) In spite of the huge mass of " experimental evidence " which has been collected, chiefly in England and in America, it appears to me that telepathy is nothing but an unproven hypothesis based upon experimental errors.

—without our being aware of the fact—by others, viz.: those which the horse required as directives for his reactions. Since this was the case, we tried to discover if a similar displacement could be brought about experimentally. The attempt was successful and we discovered that under suitable conditions we could cause the subject— quite without knowledge on his part,—to establish an " association " between any given concept and any given expressive movement. The following experimental series will serve to illustrate this fact.

I had one of the subjects (von A.) think of " left " and " right " in any order he chose. (The command was purposely given only in a general way: " Think of ' right ' or ' left ' ".). We had agreed that I was to try to guess the mental content of the subject's mind, but I was not to utter a word. Instead, I was to indicate " right " in every case by an arm movement downward, and " left " by a movement upward. To the subject I gave a fictitious but plausible reason for all this. The behavior of the subject took the following course: In the first three tests he moved his eyes to the right when he thought of " right ", and to the left when he thought of " left ". This was the normal expressive movement. In the fourth test, however, the thought " left " was accompanied by an upward movement of the eyes. Two further tests again showed eye-movements to the right and left. In the seventh test with the idea " left " the eyes moved first to the left and then immediately upward. In the following ten tests the eyes were turned regularly upward at the thought of " left ", and downward at the thought of " right ", with only one exception which was a normal movement to the left. The normal expressive movements, therefore, were displaced by the artificial, after the seventh test.

In the case of another subject (B.) in whom normally the thought of " up " was accompanied by a slight raising of the head, and " down " by a downward movement, these natural forms of expression disappeared entirely as a result of my arm movements to the right to indicate that I inferred his having in mind the thought of " up ", and to the left when I inferred that he was thinking of " down ". Instead, there appeared not merely the desired movements to the right and left, but rather movements upward to the right and downward to the left. That is, instead of a complete displacement of the old by the new, there occurred a combination of the two.

A third type of result appeared in still another subject (Ch.), who normally expressed the concepts " right " and " left " by eye or head movements (never both kinds at the same time) to the right and left. Here my arm movements up and down caused the eye and head movements to be made simultaneously, so that the thought of " right " found expression in an upward movement of the head and an eye movement to the right, and the idea of " left " in a downward head movement and a movement of the eye to the left. The subject had no knowledge of this process, and it took six tests to bring about the new reaction. From that point onward the new movements were so well established that, depending upon them for my cue, I was able to make 32 correct inferences in a total of 40 tests. During the latter part of this series I blindfolded the subject, so that I could not see the movements of his eyes, and therefore had to base my inference entirely upon his head movements.—After removing the bandage, at the end of the series, I told the subject that I would go through another series, in which I intended to indicate his thought of " right " by an arm movement downward (instead of upward as heretofore), and his thought of " left " by a movement upward. (This he regarded as an idle whim of mine). It was only after the twelfth test that the former " association " which I myself had caused to be established, was completely displaced by the new. The thought of " right " was now accompanied by an eye movement to the right and instead of a raising there was a lowering of the head. A corresponding change occurred in the head movement expressive of the thought of " left ". These responses were occasionally varied by some in which only the head movement or only the eye movement occurred. But these movements were always to the right, or downward and to the right, at the thought of " right ",—and to the left, or upward and to the left, at the thought of " left ". In ten tests I made ten correct inferences. After the new association appeared firmly established, I ceased responding by means of arm movements, and indicated my ' guesses ' by word of mouth. At first the newly acquired movements continued to appear promptly in the subjects. But gradually they tended to become more uncertain and finally disappeared, as readily as they had appeared, and the normal conditions were once more established. Nor was there any tendency to reappear on the following day in another series of tests. (Those just described had been made on one day in the course of an hour or two). But as soon as I again used the earlier method of arm movement to indicate my inferences (raising the arm for " right ", lowering it for " left "), the former artificial association was again established, although not until some 14 tests had been made,—during which the normal movements to the right and left were often inhibited and during which the conditions were, on the whole, chaotic.

The new association, thus re-established, remained constant during the ten tests of the remainder of the series, but has very probably again disappeared long ere this. In the case of this subject it appears therefore that the new associations were superimposed upon, but in no sense displaced, the normal expressive movements. Nor did the two coalesce (except in a few exceptional cases), but tended as a rule to occur independently of one another.

I would emphasize once more that none of the subjects had any knowledge of the purpose or meaning of the experiments. Also, I was convinced by questioning the subjects afterwards that none of them—and this is the essential point—had merely conceived of the arm movement which they were expecting me to make, instead of concentrating thought upon the idea of "right" or "left". On the contrary, all of them considered my particular movements mere vagaries and without purpose, and they felt perfectly certain that they were in no wise influenced by these movements. Also, none of the subjects was conscious of any movements on their part, except one, who was at times aware of her eye movements to the right, but never of those to the left, (see page 111), nor of the head movements which for us constituted the phenomena of prime interest. When I asked my subjects what they believed to be the cue upon which I based my inferences, they invariably responded with probable explanations which were always wide of the mark, and those to whom I disclosed the cue—(after the experiments were completed), were thoroughly astonished.

In the tests just described we had to do only with such ideas or concepts as normally were associated with some stereotyped form of expressive movement (see page 106).

I now chose a group of ideas which are not normally associated with a particular form of motor expression peculiarly characteristic of them, and sought to establish arti-
ficially such a connection with some arbitrary movement,
without consciousness of the process on the part of the
subject. Thus I asked one subject (Miss St.), who had
no intimation of the aim of the tests, to think of the following words in any order she might choose: " Ibis "
(ibis), " Irbis " (panther), " Kiebitz " (plover) and
" Kürbis " (pumpkin). I said that I would react to her
thoughts by means of arm movements forward and backward to the right and to the left, respectively. 15 out of
20 tests were successful, without the slightest suspicion
on the part of the subject (whose whole attention was
concentrated on the word-content), that she was giving
me the necessary directives in the form of very minute
movements of the head and eyes to the right and left, etc.
She was greatly astonished that I should be able to guess
words so much alike,—(she did not know that the element of likeness was productive of no difficulty). When,
during one of the tests, the subject happened to think
spontaneously of the movement she was expecting me to
make, she became confused, and as a result the number
of my sucessful reactions suddenly fell. I never would
have discovered the cause, had not the subject enlightened
me without my asking.

I repeated this series with three other persons, who
had had some psychological training. I did not use the
same movement for each word in all three cases, but indicated the word " Kiebitz ", for instance, by means of an
upward movement in one case, by turning the head to the
right in another, etc. In one of the three cases the tests
were almost wholly unsuccessful. The cause for this

came to light later, but it would involve too much exposition to discuss it at this point. In the case of the other two persons, the tests were successful beyond expectation. I had made my various arm movements only a few times when they presently began to raise their heads slightly when thinking of " Irbis ", and to move it to the right at the thought of " Kürbis ", etc. In the two series of 35 tests I did not have a single error. In a number of instances I succeeded in guessing the word upon which the subject had decided, even before the test proper was entered upon—i. e., before the signal for concentration had been given. Nothing surprised a subject more than the remark: " You are intending to think of the word ' Kürbis ' ", or " You had thought of concentrating your mind upon ' Ibis ' but later decided in favor of ' Kiebitz ' ", yet nothing could be more simple. Before every test the subject would consider what word he would fix upon, and while he was saying to himself " I will choose ' Ibis ' ", the proper movement would accompany his decision, although it was only very slight, because attention had not yet attained the degree of concentration which was employed in the test proper.

In these experiments also, the subjects, whom I know to be absolutely trustworthy, declared that they never thought of the arm movements which I was to make. They regarded them as being quite irrelevant. Also—with but one exception—they thought of the objects, in so far as they imaged them visually, as being directly before them, and not off in the direction indicated by my arm movements. Thus they did not image the plover (" Kiebitz ") as being on the wing, when I raised my arm, or as resting on the ground, when I pointed downward, etc. One of the subjects had done this occasionally, but by no means regularly. He was therefore asked to localize all objects in the same place, i. e., directly in front of him at the level of the eye. He complied with this request, but no change, whatever, was observed to occur in his expressive movements.

In order to overcome the difficulty just mentioned, I selected another subject (Miss von L.), whose power of visualizing was very slight, and requested her to fix her mind upon four words which I had selected because they were not, necessarily, associated with a particular image. The order in which the words were to be thought of, was entirely optional on her part. The words were " Form ", Inhalt ", " Mass ", and " Zahl ", (form, content, measure, and number), and each of them I accompanied, with a certain definite arm movement. The subject always pronounced the word inwardly as emphatically as possible, but without ever imaging the corresponding arm movement. Often, it must be noted, she did not know whether or not the movement which I made was the proper one. And yet she, too, soon fell into line in the matter of executing unconsciously the characteristic head movements. In a total of 50 tests, I was able to make 10 correct guesses in the course of the first 20 tests, 8 in the next 10 tests, and 19 in the last 20 tests. Miss von L. noted only a few of her upward head-movements, viz.: those that were especially pronounced (movements through about 2 millimeters), but of the others she knew nothing. The same experiment was repeated with a psychologist, well-trained in introspection, as a subject. Success was even greater here. But no matter how closely the subject observed himself, he was unable to solve the puzzle.

Variations which were introduced in these tests, I

will only mention in passing. Thus, instead of making an arm movement, I, in some cases, would tap with my foot, for " Ibis " once, for " Kiebitz " twice. The subject could not see my feet. The involuntary movement-expression which became associated with " Ibis " was one nod of the head, with " Kiebitz " two nods, etc. Here our only concrn was to show that unconscious change in natural expressive movements and the acquisition of artificial ones are possible in the case of psychically normal subjects trained in introspection.

I was not satisfied with convincing myself subjectively of the facts indicated, but sought to fix them objectively, by means of a graphic method. For this purpose I used the device mentioned by Prof. R. Sommer for the analysis of expressive movements.[18] The purpose for which Prof. Sommer's apparatus had been constructed, was to record the involuntary tremor and movement of the hand. These movements, of course, take place in the three dimensions of space. By means of three levers it is possible to record the movements upon the flat surface of a smoked paper fastened to the revolving drum of the kymograph, the movements in each direction being recorded by a separate lever, in such a way that the three curves thus made represent the analysis of a single movement into its three dimensional components. By making slight changes, which tended to complicate the experiment somewhat, I adapted the apparatus to the measurement of movements of the head. The method of experimentation was the following. The subject whose movements were to be registered, was placed in the device in such a way that his trunk and head were bent slightly forward, the latter a little more than the former. This, it will be remembered, was the usual position of the questioner when working with the horse. Three levers were attached to his head in such a way that every movement backward or forward would act upon the first lever, every movement to the right or left would move the second, and every movement of the head upward or downward would be recorded by the third. With regard to the sensitivity of the machine, micrometric determination showed that when the subject was properly installed, movements through so small a distance as $\frac{1}{10}$ millimeter could be accurately ascertained. The subject was carefully instructed to remain as quiet as possible, but without constraint. Voluntary movements were thus obviated. But the question arose: were not the involuntary movements thus suffering a loss?—And it was upon them that we were experimenting. The question cannot be put aside summarily, but experience taught us that the movements in question, nevertheless, did appear quite effectually, if one could have the right kind of subjects at one's command. We need hardly mention that besides the two persons immediately concerned—I, myself, attended to the apparatus—there was no one else present, and that the subject was not allowed to see the curves produced on the kymograph. Besides the registration of the head-movements, I also undertook to register the respiratory-movements of the subject. This was done by means of the so-called pneumograph, attached to which was a lever recording the thoracic expansion and contraction. This was for the purpose of ascertaining the relationship, which might eventually be found to exist, between the release of psychic tension, on the one hand, and respiration, on the other.

The subject was now told to think of some number, which, of course, was unknown to me. At a given moment I was to tap upon one of a series of keys arranged like those of a piano, with the middle finger of my right hand—corresponding to the right forefoot of the horse. The questioner observed my key, I, his head, —just what had happened in the experiments with Hans,— and as soon as I perceived the involuntary closing signal I reacted upon it by releasing, suddenly, another key upon the same keyboard, which I had in the meantime been pressing down with my second finger, thus marking what with Hans had been called the backstep. Each key was connected with a separate electro-magnet, and these in turn with markers, in such a manner that pressure upon the keys closed two electric circuits and, releasing the keys, opened them, and both the closing and the opening were recorded upon the smoked paper by means of the markers. And, finally, in order to ascertain the time relations of all these processes, a time-marker indicated the time in fifth-seconds upon the revolving kymograph record. The time-curve was recorded just below the other curves.

Of the curves * thus obtained under the most equable

---

* For registering the curves a Hering kymograph was used, with a loop 2½ metres long. The kymograph rested on felt. With the aid of the Marey model a pneumographic record was taken now of the thoracic, now of the abdominal, breathing, never both simultaneously, since this was extrinsic to my purpose, and it would have made the whole experiment too complex. The time was recorded by means of the Jacquet chronograph. For purposes of making more exact measurements the acoustic current interrupter of Bernstein was used, attuned to 100 vibrations per second. But this necessitated such rapid revolution of the drum of the kymograph that the curves were not compact enough for purposes of demonstration. The levers were all fitted with micrometer adjustments. They wrote tangentially and, except the one registering the breathing curve, all points lay in one vertical line. The error of deflection and that due to the rondure of the writing-surface,

conditions possible, we publish seven which show the great general uniformity of the tests made upon the horse with those made in the laboratory. The rôle of questioner was undertaken at different times by Mr. Schillings and the students of philosophy, Messrs. von Allesch, Chaym and K. Zoege von Manteuffel. To all of them I am greatly indebted for their unselfish services in these laborious tests. The experiments with von Allesch and Chaym, who were among the most suitable of my subjects, were conducted absolutely without knowledge on their part of the nature of the phenomena which I was observing. Neither of them knew anything about the expressive movements in which they were unconsciously indulging, and furthermore, since they kept their heads bowed during the entire course of these experiments, they did not perceive what it was that I was observing. It is interesting to note that Chaym on the occasion of his only visit to the horse, immediately received a number of correct responses. Without a doubt von Allesch would have met with equal success. The other two subjects (von M. and Sch.) went through this series of tests, possessing some knowledge of the nature of the movements involved. Conditions were such that they (and especially Mr. Schillings) could not be prevented from obtaining some

---

were both very slight on account of the comparative length of the levers and the small extent of the excursions, and for that reason synchronous points lie practically in one perpendicular. Only the breathing curve has been moved somewhat to the left, 7.5 millimeters in figures 6 and 7, 2 millimeters in figure 8, 4.5 millimeters in figure 9. (When the breathing was very profound, as occasionally happened, the error of deflection would, of course, have to be taken into account.) The curves here used as illustrations have been reproduced in the exact size of the originals by the zinco-graphic method, though somewhat compressed vertically in order to economize space.

knowledge of the essentials, at least.   However, it would be wrong to suppose that for this reason the results were more favorable, owing, mayhap, to voluntary efforts on the part of the subject.   The contrary was true.   The two subjects who had no knowledge of the character of the reactions upon which my responses depended, retained their normal habits, unchanged, throughout the series,— whereas the last-named two, afraid lest their knowledge vitiate the result, lost more and more of their power of concentration and within a short time were in a condition of tense inhibition, which is all the more conceivable, since they had had no psychological training whatever.*

Their movements, which at first were quite profuse, decreased more and more, so that in the case of von Manteuffel the percentage of my successful responses sank from 73% correct responses in 90 tests to 20% in a total of 20 tests,—and in the case of Schillings from 75-100% to 23% in a series of 35 tests.   The curves obtained with von Manteuffel as subject, which I am here publishing (figures 8 and 15), are, however, true to his normal habits.   The same is true of the two first curves of Schillings (figures 10 and 11), whereas the third (figure 12) shows distinctly the traces of the state of inhibition into which he fell, and represents the same condition as when Mr. Schillings, while preoccupied, tried to work with Hans.   All the finer details of the phenomena in question, were likewise unknown to these two subjects.

For purposes of a clearer understanding of the various

---

* My own expressive movements, on the other hand, are as pronounced as ever.   I still find the attempt to suppress them as difficult now as when I was working with the horse (page 57).   I could not, of course, procure a curve of these movements of my own.

curves, figure 5 is inserted to give the general scheme of their arrangement.

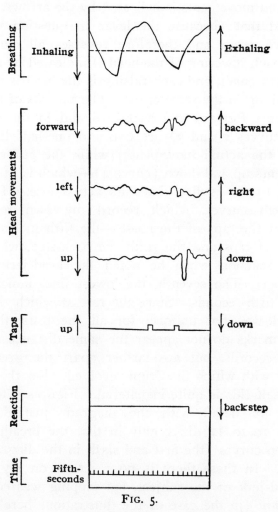

FIG. 5.

All curves are to be read like script from left to right. The first is the breathing curve of the questioner, the second, third and fourth curves represent his head movements,—all translated through the workings of the levers into up-and-down movements. The objective direction of these head movements is indicated by the arrows. It will be noted that (because the lever in question was one with two arms, and therefore reverses all movements made) each lowering of the head of indicated by a rise in the fourth curve, and each raising is the head is recorded by a sinking in the same curve. The records of the head movements forward and backward and to the left and right (curves 2 and 3) are two and one-half times the size of the actual movements; while the curve of the movements up and down (curve 4)—which is of especial interest to us—is five times its actual size. The fifth and sixth curves, which record my own responses, represent the taps of the horse,—the fifth indicating the number of taps and the sixth the back-step, which was Hans's reaction when he noted the head-jerk of the questioner. The seventh, the lowest line, indicates the time in fifth-seconds. Since the rate at which the drum revolved was not uniform for all the tests, the fifth-second marks do not appear the same distance apart in all the records, but are farther apart the greater the rapidity with which the drum revolved. For the experiment itself this is quite immaterial. Figures 6 to 9 correspond in detail with the diagram just described. Figures 10 to 12 differ only in that the breathing and back-step curves (the first and sixth in the diagram) are lacking. In these there is no response on my part to the head-jerk of the subject, but tapping was continued *ad libitum* (in the case of the illustrations here given I tapped to 5). When these latter curves were taken the ordering and the technique of the experiments had not yet been perfected. When this was finally done, Mr.

Schillings, who acted as subject in those tests, had to be eliminated from the ranks of appropriate subjects on account of the increasing inhibitions, which gradually developed as described on page 120.

Analysis of such curves is rather difficult, and those of different subjects cannot be directly compared. It is necessary to make a study of the normal curve of each subject taken when his affective state could be described as "indifferent". The influences of the purely physiological processes, such as pulse * and respiration, must also be determined. And even so, an interpretation of the curve becomes possible only when a large mass of material is at hand, and when the introspections of the subject are taken into consideration. The following remarks, therefore, are not based solely upon the illustrations given, but upon the mass total of my results.

In beginning our analysis, let us take first the breathing curve. Our results here were quite in accord with the view taken by Zoneff and Meumann,[20] who believe that in the respiration is to be found a good index of the affective tone of the subject's mental state. In the greater number of cases it was possible to conclude as to

---

* Slight head movements accompanying the pulse-beat were until recently regarded as the symptom of certain diseases of the vascular system (the so-called symptom of Nusset), but H. Frenkel has now shown them to exist also in normal individuals.[19] I myself discovered such movements (lateral as well as sagittal) more or less pronounced in all the curves obtained from my subjects. The most striking case was that of a young physician whose circulatory system was perfectly healthy. In most instances I was able to note these oscillatory movements directly and to count them without much difficulty. For purposes of control the radial pulse was always determined at the same time. The observation of the phenomenon appears to be especially easy in the case of somewhat full-blooded individuals.

the degree of concentration of attention,—and when this was very great, it was even possible to get a clue as to the number thought of.   Since the high degree of tension, under which a subject labored during a test, would be accompanied by strong affective coloring, we cannot regard as normal any of the curves here reproduced (with the exception of the two high points in figure 9). Although breathing was always deep and regular before and after a test, during the test it was less deep and irregular.   Very often it was suspended altogether (figures 7, 8 and 9).   In ordinary life we often notice that highly concentrated attention is usually accompanied by nonvoluntary inhibition of movements in the musculature which, for the moment, is not directly involved; the man lost in thought slackens his pace and finally stands still, the intent listener or looker-on holds his breath.

Of the three curves registering the movements of the head, we find that nothing peculiarly characteristic is revealed by the two upper ones, giving the movements up and down, and to the right and left, respectively. They are the ordinary tremor-like movements and indicate nothing beyond the fact that the subject is unable to hold his head absolutely quiet for even one second. It is the third line that is of interest to us, for it is here that the oft-mentioned head-jerk (which indicates arrival —in the counting—at the number expected) registers itself.   The moment of the head-jerk corresponds, almost without exception, with the moment of the first deep inhalation,—just as one would be led to expect from common experience.   But we are not to regard the head-jerk as a result of the inhalation, for it also occurs when the subject complies with the request that he hold his breath during the test.   The actual height of the jerks recorded in figures 6 to 12 was ¼ to 1½ millimeters and the average height obtained from the forty curves of these four subjects was 1 millimeter. There is great individual variation: the greatest height that was obtained from the records was $2\frac{3}{10}$ millimeters, the lowest $\frac{1}{10}$ millimeter. The variations within the records of the several individuals are comparatively slight and are evidently dependent, in the main, upon the degree of concentration of attention. Thus in the case of von Allesch, where in 75 tests the average height of the jerk is 1 millimeter, the mean variation is $\frac{4}{10}$ millimeter. If, in order to obtain some idea of the size of Mr. von Osten's movements,* we compared the values gained in the laboratory with those which would probably obtain in his case, we would say that his head movements were more minute than almost any of those of which we obtained records. At the most they could not have been more than ⅕ millimeter (when measured in terms of the distance through which the brim of his broad hat moved, they would appear to be about 1½ times as large. See page 49.) The movements of Mr. Schillings, on the other hand, were certainly four or five times as great as those of Mr. von Osten, and occasionally even greater than that. When we turn to consider the time-interval elapsing between the subject's final head-jerk and my reaction (as recorded in the sixth curve), we find that

* In a special series of experiments a subject was instructed to execute rapid head movements as minute and as evenly as possible. These were registered objectively and at the same time I made judgments concerning them. The results showed that my judgments were most exact in the case of the most minute jerks. The thing that made it especially easy to judge the movements of Mr. von Osten under normal conditions, (page 220), was their extraordinary evenness, such as I have not met with in any other individual.

the reaction-time averages $\frac{3}{10}$ seconds, a value which
agrees very favorably with that estimated for the horse

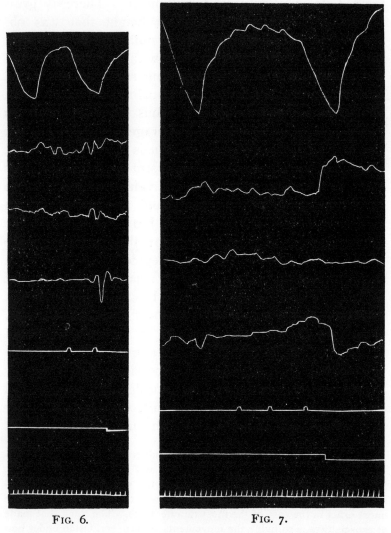

FIG. 6.   FIG. 7.

(page 56). Thus it appears that man and beast have
the same reaction-time—though we must bear in mind

that I worked under some difficulty, since I had to care for the apparatus.

Let us now turn to a discussion of the several figures.

Figure 6 (von Allesch) gives a typical view of the great, and at the same time economic concentration of attention characteristic of the subject. Respiration (first curve) is not so profound as usual, yet is changed very little. The head-jerk (fourth curve) is of medium height. It occurs just at the proper moment,—the subject had thought of 2, and had directed his attention economically. This attention was of the kind described as type I. on page 93. The lowering of the head, (recorded in the figure by a rise in the curve), immediately following upon the head-jerk upward, is irrelevant.

In figure 7 (Chaym) we have a record of a different nature. Respiration was inhibited throughout the test,— (the small waves are due to the pulsating of the heart) ; immediately after the test deep breathing takes place. Tension steadily increased till 3, the number expected, was reached. The head, accordingly, gradually sank a little forward. The head-jerk ensued during an interval beginning just before the reaching of the goal and ended immediately after. The movement was predominantly backward, its upward direction being only through a distance of $\frac{1}{4}$ millimeter. (This subject was not so strongly motor as the preceding one.) The reaction followed promptly as seen in curve 6. It was the decided raising of the head which follows the head-jerk, that prevented the usual back-step with the left foot, when the subject was working with Hans.

Figure 8 (von Manteuffel) is typical of strong and at the same time economical concentration. Respiration, normally deep and very regular, is for a time completely inhibited. Tension rises steadily and the head gradually inclines forward. In the interval between the number

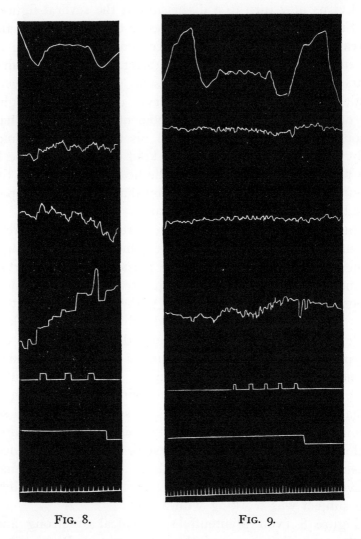

FIG. 8.   FIG. 9.

before the final one and the final one the subject makes a sudden bend forward and immediately upon reaching the final number gives a violent jerk of the head, upward. The attention here would be characterized as being of type III, described on page 94. (Owing to lack of space it is impossible to give an example of type II, which is only to be found in the case of very large numbers.)

Figure 9 (von Allesch) is expressive of great, but—according to the subject's introspection—not economical concentration. Respiration, which before and after the test was quite regular, during the test itself shows a

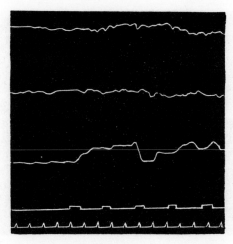

FIG. 10.

pause. (The tiny waves are due to the heart-beat.) The subject had thought of 5, and this number is accompanied by a decided head-jerk. But we note that even before the final jerk a number of less pronounced jerks occur— the result of poorly regulated psychic tension.

Figure 10 (Schillings) depicts a very high degree of uneconomical concentration. There was sudden concentration at the beginning of the test, and a steady increase throughout its course. Accordingly Mr. Schillings bent

forward at the start, and inclined still farther forward
at the second—and just before the third—tap. But
at 3 there is a sudden upward jerk. The number
thought of had been 4, tension therefore had exploded, as
it were, too soon.

Figure 11 (again of Schillings) gives indications, on
the other hand, of a medium and economic concentration
of attention, which is more normal in character. The
number thought of was 4.

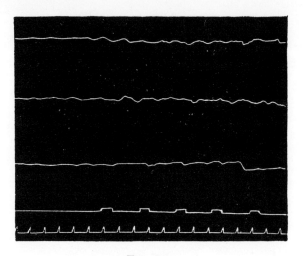

Fig. 11.

Figure 12 (Schillings again) is indicative of a low
degree of psychic tension. With the very first tap the
head begins to rise and continues to do so throughout
the test. A true final jerk does not occur, we note rather
in all three curves registering the head movements, slight
time-marking movements, especially in the second curve.
In the third curve they are at first minute, but increase
steadily in size until the fourth tap, after which they
suddenly disappear. The subject had, as a matter of fact,

thought of the number 4, but it is hardly probable that Hans would have reacted properly upon these stimuli.

Mr. Schillings had thought of the same number in all three tests given in figures 10, 11 and 12. The probabilities are that if he had been working with the horse at the time, in the first case Hans would have reacted with three taps with the right foot and a final tap with the left, as a result of the questioner's bending forward again after the premature head-jerk at 3. In the second in-

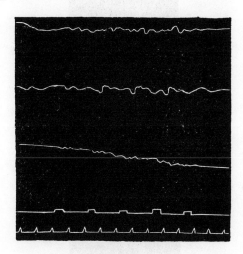

FIG. 12.

stance the horse would probably have given four taps with the right foot, and in the third, the chances are that he would have continued to tap beyond the 4.

These curves give, on the whole, a fair idea of the intensity and of the course of attention of the various subjects.

Let us now consider a number of records which illustrate the expressive movements involved in the process of thinking of such concepts as " up ", " down ", etc.

Their arrangement is identical with the scheme given in figure 5, with the exception that the tapping curves (the sixth and seventh) do not appear. The subject was asked to think of any of the words "up", "down", "right", "left", "yes", "no", etc. He was to begin to conceive

FIG. 13.

them vividly when the command "Now!" was given. This moment is recorded in figures 13 to 15 on the fifth curve. What has been said on page 123 with regard to respiration, holds also in these instances: only the first rise recorded in figure 14 can be regarded as normal.

The magnitude of these movements varies between $\frac{1}{2}$ and 3 millimeters. The records of the subject whose movements were most extensive, show an average of $1\frac{7}{10}$ millimeter (based on 50 tests), with a mean variation of $\frac{6}{10}$ millimeter. Lack of space precludes the reproduction of more than three records.

Figure 13 (von Allesch) shows the movement accompanying the thought of " up ", a slight raise of the head, recorded in the fourth curve. (The thought of " down " is accompanied by a corresponding downward movement.)

Figures 14 (von Allesch) and 15 (von Manteuffel) illustrate the nod which is associated with the thought of " yes " in the case of two subjects. It is essentially the same in both: the head is lowered and then raised. The first of the two subjects is more decidedly motor, and his movements therefore were somewhat the more extensive. In the case of the second subject the nod proper is followed by another which is somewhat less extensive.

A number of other experiments were carried out which corresponded with the color-selecting tests made upon Hans. (Page 78.) Five sheets of white paper, $\frac{1}{2}$ meter long and $\frac{1}{4}$ meter wide, were arranged in a series upon the floor, $\frac{1}{4}$ meter apart. A dot marked the middle of each. The experimenter stood at a distance of $7\frac{1}{2}$ meters and directly opposite the middle sheet. At about $\frac{1}{2}$ meter to the right or left of him stood the subject who took the part of the " horse ". The problem of the experimenter was to indicate to the " horse " a certain one of the five sheets, but without the use of word or gesture. I at first undertook the rôle of " horse ", whereas the others consecutively played the part of questioner. All of them looked fixedly at the sheet which they had in mind. Besides, it usually happened that they would turn at least their heads, and often their bodies, more or less

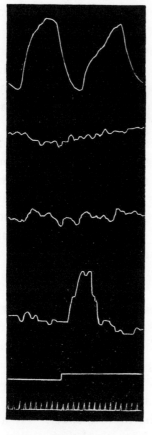

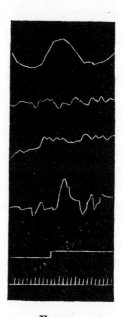

Fig. 14.   Fig. 15.

in the direction of the particular sheet—and this without purpose or knowledge on their part, but purely as a result of concentration upon the sheet they wished me to point out. One of the experimenters remarked, quite casually, that he had noted that I always made a better judgment, the more intently he thought of the sheet. Others often admitted that, when I had made an error, they had not imagined the sheet vividly, or had been debating whether or not to decide to think of the neighboring sheet—the one I had designated. This indecision could be noticed by the direction of the eyes. But the following table shows how uniform, on the whole, was the behavior of the various persons when under the guidance of the same impulse. The number of tests was 200 in each case. All errors were of the same character. Neighboring sheets were mistaken for each other, and the errors were never of more than one position to either side. Their number can easily be obtained by subtracting the percentage of correct inferences from the total, 100%.

Experimenter:	v. A.	B.	C.	Mrs. v. H.	K.	Miss v. L.
Correct inferences:	88%	88%	77%	81%	77%	82%

It will be seen that the number of correct interpretations is quite high and in none of the cases does it deviate far from the mean average of 82%.

I based my judgment as to the direction of the subject's eyes, upon an imaginary line perpendicular to the center of the cornea. (This perpendicular does not always coincide with the subject's line of vision, which was the thing I was after, but this cannot be directly obtained. This, of course, was what made the judgment a rather difficult matter.) My judgment as to the direction of the head I based largely on the direction of the nose, (to express it more accurately: upon the direction of the median plane.) I purposely noted only the position of the experimenter and not the movement which led up to to it.   When I tried to do the latter, the results were not always satisfactory, because the head and eyes of the person would frequently, in the process of adjustment, move beyond the goal and thus lead me into error.   An attempt was made to make each judgment as independent as possible of the preceding one.   But usually, after a few tests, an unintentional association became established between certain attitudes and the different places in the series of papers.   Often all that was necessary was to observe the experimenter in order to know which of the places he had in mind, it was not necessary to look at the papers at all.   Every change in the position of the person would, of course, make the association thus established, useless.

Later, the subjects and I changed rôles, I took the part of the experimenter and they the part of the "horse".   The number of tests in each case was 200 as before.   Here, too, errors were, with but one exception, never more than of one place to either side. Whether the error was one place to the right or one place to the left appeared to depend upon the position of the person making the judgment, i. e., it depended on whether he stood at my right or at my left.   The following results were obtained:

Subject ("horse"):	v. A.	B.	C.	Mrs. v. H.	K.	Miss v. L.
Correct inferences :	76%	79%	75%	81%	77%	74%

A certain agreement can be seen in these results.   The average of correct inferences is somewhat lower than that which was obtained by me (page 135), 77% as over against 82%.   This is probably due to the fact that the subjects had had so little practice compared with me.

With one of these subjects, Mr. Koffka, a student of

philosophy, I carried these tests somewhat further, varying them partly by increasing the number of sheets of
paper, partly by decreasing the distance between them.
The increase in the number of sheets made only a slight
difference in the results.   With 200 tests in each case I
obtained the following results:

No. of sheets	:	5	6	7	8	9	10
Correct inferences	:	77%	72%	72%	69%	73%	68%

With but few exceptions, the errors were, as a rule, of
one place.   The series with an odd number of sheets (5,
7, 9) gave better results than those with an even number
(6, 8, 10).   In the tests with the odd number of sheets
the experimenter (K.) stood in front of the middle sheet,
so that it was at the apex of a right angle made by the
series of papers and the median plane of the subject's
body; whereas in the case of the even number of papers
the subject stood opposite the space between the two
middle sheets, thus making the position of the sheets less
favorable.

In the preceding tests the distance between the centers
of the neighboring sheets was always 50 centimeters, so
that the angle through which the median plane of the experimenter's body would have to turn in order to pass
from one sheet to the next, was about 3¾ degrees.   In
the following tests these distances were gradually
decreased.   The sheets, always five in number, were
replaced by ever narrower white strips of paper mounted
on dark cardboard and illumined by a Nernst lamp.
The following table shows the decrease in correct inferences running parallel with the decrease of the angle
through which the subject would have to turn in order
to be in line with the several pieces of a series succes-

sively. The percentage in each case is based upon at least 100 tests.

Angle:	$3\frac{3}{4}°$	$3°$	$2\frac{1}{2}°$	$2°$	$1\frac{1}{2}°$	$1°$
Distance between the centres of two neighboring papers:	50cm	39cm.	33cm.	26cm.	20cm.	13cm.
No. of correct inferences:	77%	73%	71%	68%	66%	61%

A curious and unexpected change was here noted in the subject, Mr. Koffka, who, while concentrating his attention to the uttermost, began unawares to develop a new system of expressive movements of the head. When the distance between the sheets was relatively great, he had been in the habit of turning his head and eyes in the direction of the sheet intended, and as the distances became less he had reacted only by a turning of the eyes. But now, as the distances were still further decreased, he began again to react by means of head movements, and these were of exaggerated magnitude, for which he would compensate, as it were, by an eye-movement in the opposite direction. Although the head movements decreased in scope as the distances between the sheets were steadily decreased, they still were always decidedly greater than the eye movements, which I was now normally led to expect and which could be judged without much difficulty. This form of reaction was much more satisfactory as a cue, and therefore it came to pass that, whereas in the preceding series I had made only 60% correct inferences when the angle was 1 degree, I now found that—the angle remaining the same—80% of my inferences were correct. (My final judgment I continued to base, as before, upon the position, and not upon the movement, of head and eye). The number of correct inferences continued relatively high, even after the distance between the papers was decreased tenfold,—as will be seen from the following table:

Angle:	.	.	.	1°	30′	15′	9′	7′	6′	5′	3′	2′
Distance between the centres of two neighboring papers:		.	.	131	65	33	20	15	13	11	6½	4mm.
Percentage of correct inferences:	.		. .	80	79	78	81	84	80	77	68	68%

Beginning with an angle of 1′ (distance between the centers of two neighboring papers = 2 mm.), the subject was unable to focus, with sufficient steadiness of vision, upon one paper alone, and the movements, for that reason, ceased to manifest themselves. Comparing the results obtained in the case of this subject with those obtained from two others, whose reactions had remained normal, B. and Miss St., we find that with them there were only 53% correct inferences in both cases (based each upon 200 tests), when the angle was 5′. In my errors, too, I often shot wider of the mark. In another series of 200 tests, in which Miss St. " merely thought of the places ", I had a percentage of 56% correct inferences, and my errors did not become any coarser. Miss St. believed this a case of true telepathy, but I had been guided in my judgments entirely by her unwittingly made movements—or rather the direction—of her eyes. The magnitude of these movements bore a constant relationship to the distance between papers as it was conceived by the subject.

Reviewing the experiments discussed in this chapter, we find that the same kind of movements and postures, which had been noted in persons experimenting with the horse, tended to recur in the laboratory, in so far as the mental attitude of the subjects, given in their introspective accounts, corresponded with that of the questioners of the horse.

CHAPTER V

EXPLANATION OF THE OBSERVATIONS

THE author having described the observations made upon the horse, and having discussed the activities of the questioner upon the basis of observations made objectively and upon his own introspections, and having verified the results thus obtained, by means of laboratory tests,—we are now in a position to solve satisfactorily all the problems which this interesting case has presented.

That which is least difficult to understand is the horse's seeming knowledge of language and particularly his ability to answer questions, no matter by whom, or in what dialect, they were put. As a matter of fact, it made no difference who desired an answer, for the only person upon whom the experiment depended was the questioner, that is, the one who asked the horse to tap. We have everywhere designated this person as the experimenter or questioner. It was he who gave the directions, and since all that were involved were visual signs, the drama in which Hans appeared as the hero, was nothing but a pantomime. All speech was superfluous and, except in so far as the tone of voice in which it was spoken was soothing or reprimanding, it was quite unintelligible to the horse.

From the foregoing, the reader understands without further explanation Hans's ability to count and to make computations. If the number of taps had depended solely upon the length of time and the angle at which the questioner bent forward, the horse would have been able to tap any number desired. Since, however, only the right foot was employed, the left one being used at most for making a final tap, the number of taps had an upper limit which was due to the fatigue of the animal. This limit was about 100. That it was possible to ask such questions as: "How many times is 100,000 contained in 654321?", and thus to give problems involving millions, is perfectly clear.

All wonderful feats of counting and computation which were accomplished while thus experimenting with the horse are to be accredited, not to the horse, but to the questioner. If such is the case, they certainly cannot be considered astonishing. Thus, when to the question, "How many of the gentlemen present are wearing straw hats?" the horse answers correctly in accordance with the wording of the question and omits the straw hat of a lady, then Mr. von Osten is the guide. It is no wonder that Hans never showed the slightest excitement when confronted with difficult problems, nor that it apparently took no time whatever to solve them.

Hans, however, was also a faithful mirror of all the errors of the questioner. Aside from mistakes due to occasional interruptions on the part of visitors, these errors had two sources: faulty computation and inadequate concentration—i. e., aside from arithmetical errors on the part of the questioner, were his premature or belated movements. Since both of these factors might be operative, the following three possibilities arise.

(a) The questioner computes correctly but does not move at the proper moment. Nearly all the errors which had been accredited to the horse, were of this kind.

A part of these errors had the appearance of being

significant, that is, they might be interpreted as a mis-apprehension of the question.   If, for instance, instead of a sum only one of the quantities was given, or, if instead of a product only one of the factors was given, it might be interpreted that the horse simply wished to repeat the problem.   Thus, Mr. von Osten in response to the question: " How much is 3 times 5 ? ", twice in succession received the answer, " 3 ", and upon my question, " How much is 3 plus 4 ? " he answered, " 3 ", and to " How much is 2 times 6 ? " he tapped 6, and to " What is one-fourth of 36 ? " 4.   In part (certainly in the second and third example cited) an individual quantity or factor had been emphasized in the consciousness of the questioner (cf. page 105) and in part the reactions were due to chance.   Thus, when Mr. Hahn asked the question: " What is one-half of 10 ? ", he received the following responses: 2 and 10, and then 17 and 3.   To this class belong also, the tests made by the Commission of September and reported in Supplement III.   (See page 255).

Other errors, even though they may not have appeared to be significant, might yet have been characterized as mistakes due to speed; as when, e. g., Hans made an error of one unit—and sometimes, though less frequently, of two units—too much or too little in his response.   One might be led to believe that Hans had not made an error of calculation but merely of counting in the process of giving his result, which always had to be done by the cumbersome method of tapping.   As a matter of fact, the trouble lay in the wrong degree of concentration on the part of the questioner: In errors of $+$ 1, tension was too slight, in those of $-$ 1, it was too great (see page 91).   This comes out clearly in a comparison of the two more extensive series which I took in the case of Mr. Schil-

lings. During the first series, he was well disposed, and
was able to concentrate effectively, while during the
second, he was nervous and easily diverted. This difference in intensity of concentration in the case of the
two series is attested, not only subjectively by Mr. Schillings's introspective statement, but may be measured
objectively by means of the number of final taps which
the horse gave with his left foot during these two series.
We saw (page 94) that these final taps were always a
sign of intense concentration and, as a matter of fact,
one-half of the horse's responses to Mr. Schillings during
the first series were made in this way; whereas, in the
second series, only one-third were of this sort.   (I, myself, was never able to get, without conscious control, a
greater number of this type of response.)   We may
therefore say that, in the first series we had a high degree
of tension, or concentration, whereas, in the second
series, we had a low degree.   The errors distribute themselves over the two series as follows:

	+1	+2	−1	−2
Series I (31 tests)				
Correct responses : 87%				
Incorrect " :	0%	0%	13%	0%
Series II (40 tests)				
Correct responses : 40%.				
Incorrect " :	40%	8%	2.5%	0% (and 9.5% other kinds of errors.)

We find in Series I no " + 1 " errors, but only " — 1 "
errors; in series II, on the other hand, the errors are
almost exclusively of the " + 1 " category, equaling the
number of correct responses, and there is only one
" — 1 " error. A series obtained in the case of Mr. von
Osten is almost as satisfactory an illustration. When he

first began to take part in tests in which the procedure was the one we characterized as " without knowledge " and had to note their complete failure, he was thrown into such confusion that the responses in the case of procedure with knowledge were also incorrect.   The errors there were always $+$ 1, (whereas those in the case of procedure with knowledge, which were due to quite different causes, were very great and inconstant.)   The number of $+$ 1 errors obtained on this occasion comprises one-fourth of all the plus errors which were ever obtained in the case of Mr. von Osten during the entire course of these experiments.   Finally, I would mention two examples of my own.   In the course of my very first attempts with Hans I obtained, as I said on page 89, three responses in a total of five which exceeded the correct result by 1.   This I would explain by the fact that although I employed a high degree of concentration, I nevertheless was somewhat skeptical.   The result was a certain deficiency in the degree of concentration.   A second example which I would cite is taken from the period in which I had already discovered the cue to Hans's reactions and goes to show that I was then still able to eliminate the influence of this knowledge and to work ingenuously.   To the question, " How much is 9 less 1 ? "   I, momentarily indisposed, received the answer 10, and then six times in succession the answer " 9 ", and finally the correct response, " 8 ".

Errors of another kind—the not infrequent offenses against the very elements of counting and the fundamental arithmetical processes—were regarded in part as intentional jokes and by an authority in pedagogy as a " sign of independence and stubbornness which might also be called humor ".   Hans emphatically asserted that

2+2 was 3 or he would answer questions given in immediate succession as follows: " How many eyes have
you?—2. " How many ears? "—2. " How many tails? "
—2. These errors, as a matter of fact, evince neither
wit nor humor, but prove incontrovertibly that Hans had
not even mastered the fundamentals.

Many of the errors baffle every charitable attempt at
interpretation. These gave the horse the reputation of
capriciousness and unreliability. If Hans designated the
tone " e " as the seventeenth, or " g " as the eleventh, or
when he called Friday the 35th day of the week or
believed 50 pfennige to be worth only 48, the cause for
these responses lay either in the insufficient degree of
tension on the part of the questioner (as in the first
three examples) or in the extravagant expenditure of the
same (as in the last case). If, therefore, the horse
at times would " hopelessly flounder " which would seem
to be indicated by tapping now with the right and now
with the left foot, then as a matter of fact, this form of
reaction came about as was described on page 61, with
this difference that there we had to do with voluntary
controlled movements on the part of the questioner,
whereas here, they are the result of an unsuitable degree
of tension which expressed itself in frequent and disconcerting jerks. Besides the answer 3, this so-called
floundering was the only reaction the average person
could obtain from the horse in the absence of Mr. von
Osten and Mr. Schillings. It would however occur
also in the case of these gentlemen and would be received by them with resentment when in truth it was
Hans's greatest feat, for he showed his extremely keen
reaction upon every movement of the questioner. To
this group belong also the errors in the case of higher

numbers, the sole cause of which lay in the difficulty with which tension could be maintained and the body kept motionless for so long a period. These errors occurred in accordance with a certain law. If, for instance, a certain test repeatedly evoked incorrect responses, the questioner would gradually increase the duration of tension and would thus come a little nearer to the desired goal with every test. In this way, Mr. von Osten desiring 30 as an answer obtained consecutively the responses, 25, 28, 30; and I, myself, for the answer 20, received consecutively the responses 10, 18, 20 (see also the laboratory tests, page 105). Sometimes too, the questioner would flag in his efforts before the goal was reached. Thus in one of my first tests, I received for the answer 11 the following responses: 1, 4, 5, 7, 4. I was unable to get beyond 7. In other instances, the horse responded first with too few and then with too many taps. The correct response therefore could only be obtained after an appreciable amount of gauging of tension, as in target practice there must be a gauging of distance. (See page 92). In this way Mr. von Osten obtained for 10 the responses 8, 8, 11, 10, and Mr. Schillings for 17, received 9, 16, 19, 18, 18, 14, 9, 9, and finally, after some efforts, 17 taps. Thus there was a rise from 9 to 19, then a fall back to 9 and after eight tests the correct response. As long as we attempt to explain this fact as error on the part of the horse, so long will it remain inexplicable, but the moment we regard it from the point of view of the psychology of the tension of expectation, it becomes perfectly plain.

The same holds true for the curious predilection which Hans appeared to have for the numbers from 2 to 4, especially for 3 (see page 68). As a matter of fact the

cause of this lies in nothing other than the inadequate concentration of attention on the part of the questioner and
less often in an extravagant expenditure of concentration,
which explodes immediately after the first tap on the
part of Hans (as in the case of my first tests) ; but usually the cause lay in a complete lack of concentration,
though the same result may be produced by various
causes. It is usually after 2 to 4 taps of the horse's foot
that the questioner, who does not concentrate, makes his
first move which naturally puts an end to the tapping
on the part of the horse. As a rule this jerk follows immediately upon the second tap. (On the other hand, relaxation of attention is very difficult upon the first tap.
See page 95). The questioner, however, would expect
further tapping and therefore would not bring his body
back to a completely erect position and the result would
be a 3, the last unit of which would be given by the
final tap with the left foot. Here we also obtained light
as to the answers which Hans gave in those tests in
which the method was that of "procedure without
knowledge". These responses had nothing to do with
the problem, for neither the horse nor any one else knew
the solution. But in the horse's responses the degree of
tension of the questioner's concentration was faithfully
mirrored. An experimenter who was as skillful in concentrating as Mr. von Osten, obtained—almost without
exception—very high numbers, whereas one whose concentration was slight would receive in response to nearly
all questions the answers 2, 3 or 4. Thus, the Count zu
Castell received in response to seventeen questions the answer 2, three times, the answer 3, six times, and the
answer 4, four times, two answers being accidentally correct.

Another group of errors was characterized as stubbornness on the part of Hans, such as his persistence in repeating an incorrect response, or his repetition of a former correct answer in response to later questions where it was perfectly senseless. During a demonstration before a large number of persons, I held a slate with the number 13 upon it within the horse's view and also within view of the spectators. I, myself, did not know what number was written on the slate. Having been asked to tap the number, Hans responded by tapping 5. The grand-stand shouted " Wrong! " I asked Hans to try again. Four times in succession he answered 5. At another time Mr. von Osten and I each whispered a number (7 and 1, respectively,) into the horse's ear and asked him to add the two. Three times in succession he tapped 11. After the test had been repeated in accordance with "procedure with knowledge" and a correct response had been received, we tried once more a test of " procedure without knowledge ". Again, he responded with an 11. On a third occasion, I asked Hans to tap 5. He responded with a 4 and then, correctly, with a 5. Thereupon, I asked him to tap 6. Again, he responded with a 4. Then I asked him to tap 7. Once more he responded with a 4, and only when I proceeded to count aloud did he tap 7 correctly. I had him repeat the 7 and then went over to 9. Promptly he responded with another 7. In these cases, which by-the-way were not very frequent, we have to do, not with stubbornness on the part of Hans, but with the persistence of that number in the consciousness of the questioner. Modern psychology has recognized this tendency of ideas, which have once been in consciousness, to reappear on other occasions even though they are wholly inappropriate.

It has been termed " perseverative tendency." (Persever-ationstendenz ").[21]

While the errors thus far discussed appeared sporadi-cally in long series of correct responses, there still might be observed at times a massing of errors, usually at the beginning of a day of experimentation or at the begin-ning of a new series. We were regularly told that Hans always had to have time to adjust himself to new cir-cumstances. The records often showed comments such as these: " After a number of practice tests the horse appears particularly well disposed ", or " Hans, at first inattentive, does not respond. Suddenly he gets the hang of things ". Different questioners who worked with the horse required different lengths of time to obtain proper responses. Some needed a quarter of an hour, others scarcely half a minute. I, myself, found that in the degree in which I learned to control my attention, in that degree did this phenomenon tend to disappear, but would reappear the moment I became indisposed. From this we see that, instead of attributing all sorts of mental characteristics, such as stubbornness, etc., to the horse, we should lay them to the account of the questioner. As a matter of fact we find that this " getting into the sweep of things ", i. e. the overcoming of psycho-physical inertia, has long been known in the case of man and has been experimentally determined and called " Anregung " (excitation) by the psychiatrist, Kraepelin,[22] and his pupil, Amberg.[23] A massing of errors toward the end of a long series occurred only when the questioner was fatigued. There was nothing which had to be interpreted as fatigue or as indisposition on the part of the horse, (except in the few cases of very large numbers, cf. page 67). To be sure, Mr. von Osten always offered these two excuses. That they were without warrant is shown by the fact that Hans, after appearing indisposed or fatigued while working with one questioner, would nevertheless react promptly and correctly a moment later for some other experimenter, and furthermore, when working with me, the number of his correct responses would rise or fall with my own mental disposition.

Finally, I would here note a rather interesting observation for which I am indebted to Mr. Schillings and the Count zu Castell. They had noticed, independently of each other, that the horse would often fail to react when for any length of time he was given problems dealing with abstract numbers, even though they were of the simplest kind; but that he would immediately improve whenever the questions had to do with concrete objects. They believed that Hans found applied mathematics more interesting, and that abstract problems, or those which were altogether too elementary, bored him. The Count zu Castell furthermore noticed that the responses tended to be more correct as soon as he had the horse count objects which he, himself, (Castell) could see during the test. Quite in accord with this is the statement to be found in the report of the September-Commission, in which we find this note in a discussion of the arithmetical problems (not involving visible objects), which the gentlemen already mentioned had given the horse. " The horse responded with less and less attentiveness and appeared to play with the questioner." Here again, that was looked for in the animal which should have been sought in the man. Mr. Schillings was capable of intense, but not continued concentration and it was he who was bored, and not the horse. And it was the Count zu Castell and not the horse that found it necessary to invoke the aid of perceptual objects to bring his attention to the proper height of concentration.

The reader will see that thus far I have supposed the horse to be a never-failing mechanism and that I have placed all errors to the account of the questioner. The horse never failed to note the signal for stopping and therefore never was the immediate cause of an error. It is not to be denied that now and then he would cease tapping spontaneously and in this way would become the cause of an error. We have no data on this point, but undoubtedly the horse's share in the total number of errors was very slight.

(*b.*) Another source of error was faulty computation on the part of the questioner. The questioner made the signal for stopping when the expected number of taps had been reached. The horse faithfully mirrored the miscalculation of the questioner. I have knowledge of only one such case. The journals report that once Mr. von Osten, when someone called to his attention that Hans had indicated the wrong day of the week, replied: " Yes, you are right, it was not Thursday, but Friday," whereupon Hans being asked again, promptly responded correctly. This appeared to the reporter in question as proof of the subjective influence of Mr. von Osten upon the horse.

(*c.*) When errors in calculation and failures in proper concentration combine, i. e. when the questioner makes a mistake in calculation because he is excited or inattentive and for the same reason does not make the movement, which is the signal for stopping, in accordance with the number which he deems to be the correct answer, then the result is usually wrong, but it may be correct in the few cases in which the two errors exactly compensate each other. Nothing has been so effective in establishing Hans's reputation, nothing has brought him so many followers, as these cases in which he, rather than his mentor, has been in the right. Compared with the mass of cases in which Hans was wrong these latter cases are diminishingly few in number, yet these few made such an impression upon the observers that their number tended to be overestimated. As a matter of fact, I have been able to discover records of only seven such cases. Two of these were reported by the Count zu Castell. On the 8th of September, he entered the horse's stall, alone, and believing it to be the seventh day of the month, he asked Hans the date. The horse responded correctly with 8 taps. At another time he held up before Hans a slate on which were written the numbers 5, 8 and 3 and asked the horse to indicate their sum which in the momentary excitement, vaguely appeared to Castell to be 10. To his chagrin he noticed that Hans continued to tap. Thereupon he intentionally remained motionless until the horse had stopped tapping spontaneously—as he thought—at 16. (The newspapers reported that the numbers to be added had been 5, 3, and 2; that the questioner had expected the answer 11, but that Hans had in three tests always ceased tapping at 10.) In both cases the questioner regarded the answers of the horse as wrong and recognized his mistake when his attention was called to it. I, myself, had the same experience. One time I received in response to the question, "What day of the week is Monday?", the answer 2, although I had expected the answer 1; at another time I asked, "How much is 16 less 9?", and the horse responded with 7 taps, although I had erroneously expected 5. I noticed my mistake only when my attention was called to it by one of those present. Another example is related by Mr. Schillings. A row of colored cloths lay before Hans. Beside them stood an army officer. Pointing to the latter's red coat Mr. Schillings asked the horse to indicate, by means of tapping, the place in the row where a piece of the same color lay. Hans tapped eight times, but Mr. Schillings reprimanded him because the red piece was, as a matter of fact, second in the row. Upon a repetition of the test, Hans again tapped 8. (By some, the facts are recounted as having been the other way round; viz.: Hans tapped 2 instead of 8. This of course would call for a different explanation.) It was noticed that at the place which would be indicated by eight taps there was not a red piece but a carmine colored piece of cloth. A newspaper reports, somewhat vaguely, a sixth case as follows: Hans was asked to spell the name "Dönhoff" and began correctly: "Dö". Mr. von Osten, who somehow began to think of another name, "Dohna", interrupted him and wished to correct him by suggesting o instead of ö (i. e., 2 taps instead of 3). Hans, however, "continued to spell the entire word with the greatest equanimity. He had not erred. A similar experience is reported by Mr. H. von Tepper-Laski, the well known hippologist. Although the details have slipped from his memory, he reports that in the case in question the correct answer was thrice refused by the questioner who thought that the horse's answer was incorrect. Hans, upon being severely reprimanded in a loud and harsh tone of voice, turned about as if disgusted with the injustice of the man and made straight for his stall.—It is clear that in the cases described we are not dealing with accidentally correct responses, for in nearly every case the test was repeated a number of times and the same responses were received each time. As a matter of fact, my own introspection convinced me that the third and fourth cases were surely, and the first and sixth were very probably, due to insufficient concentration on the part of the questioner. Accordingly there is everywhere in these cases a difference of $+ 1$ or $+ 2$ between the number thought of and the number tapped (see page 92 f.). The data in the second and fifth and still more in the seventh case were too meager to warrant an attempt at explanation, for it is not even known whether Hans responded with more or fewer taps than was expected by the questioner. It is unfortunate that a more complete record was not made.

The frequent and intentional attempts of Mr. von Osten to induce the horse to give an incorrect response, —which, by-the-way, were regularly unsuccessful—belong only apparently to this group. Thus he asked, e. g., " 2 times 2 is 5, is it not? " " 3 times 3 is 8? ", etc., but Hans refused to be misled, and responded correctly. This was from the very beginning one of the main arguments for independent thinking on the part of the horse. The actual procedure was as follows, even though the questioner had said " 2 times 2 is 5 ", there still was present in his consciousness the number 4. I, myself, would think either of the first member of the equation, i. e., 2 times 2, in which case Hans would respond with 4 taps or I would have in mind the second member, i. e., 5, in which case he would respond with 5 taps. Never did I succeed in thinking of both at the same time. The association between the thought " 2 times 2 " and the concept " 4 " is so close and supported by so many other associations that the attempt to form a new one, that is at complete variance with all these, is futile. One may say " 2 times 2 equals 5 " but it is impossible to conceive it.

Let us turn now, from the tests in counting and computation to those in reading. We have seen that Hans manifested his seeming knowledge of language symbols in a threefold manner: he might approach a slate on which was written the symbol asked for, or he would indicate its location in a series of slates by means of tapping, or finally by means of so-called spelling of the word which was written upon a slate or placard. The responses by means of approaching a placard were very often unsuccessful, while indications by means of tapping were scarcely ever unsuccessful. If it were true that higher intellectual proceesses * were here involved, then the converse would have been expected, for tapping required not only the ability to read, but also the ability to count. If, on the other hand, we assume that the horse simply followed the directions given by the questioner's movements, this seeming difficulty resolves itself, for it would be more difficult for Hans to perceive the signs which he receives while moving than those which he receives while tapping. When we recall that it was easier

---

* Professor Shaler [24], a well-known American savant, mentions a three-year old pig belonging to a Virginian farmer, that was able to read and had some understanding of language. From numerals which were written upon cards and spread out before it, this pig could compose dates. It could also select from among certain cards one upon which was written a given name, asked for by the master. Supposedly no signs of any kind were given. (Shaler thought to exclude effectively the sense of smell, which is so highly developed in the pig, in that he, Shaler, himself smelled at the cards, since he also "possessed an acute olfactory sense!") Since we are told that the farmer in question made a business of supplying trained pigs for exhibition purposes, the case appears suspicious. We hear of a pig exhibited in London, that was able to read and spell, and could also tell the time by the watch [25]. We cannot tell, however, whether the two pigs, which beyond a doubt were mechanically trained to respond to signals, are identical or not.

to direct the horse to a placard near the end of a row than one nearer the center (see page 81), we can readily understand how it was that during the experimentation carried on by the September-Commission (Supplement III; page 255), Hans was able to point out immediately the placards on which were written the names " Castell " and " Stumpf ", for they were at the two extreme ends, but was unsuccessful in locating the one on which was written the name " Miessner " which was not a bit more difficult to read, but was located at the fourth place in the row.   He first approached the fifth card, then upon repetition of the test he pointed out the other neighboring tablet, viz., the third.

In spelling, Hans was quite indifferent whether his table with the eighty-four number signs upon it stood before him, for he had no knowledge of letters. Neither Mr. von Osten nor Mr. Schillings required it, for the former knew the table by heart and Mr. Schillings told me that before every test he made a note of the numbers which were necessary to indicate the required letters, trusting in this way to control the responses of the horse and never guessing that by so doing he was making it possible for the horse to answer correctly.   The newspaper reports aroused much interest at the time by stating that Hans was able to spell such proper names as " Plüskow " and " Bethmann-Hollweg ", even to putting in the difficult " w " and " th ".   The friends of Mr. von Osten at the same time called attention to the exquisite auditory acuteness of the horse which enabled him to perceive the aspirated " w " and to discriminate between the " th " and " t ", (the " th " is softer than the " t " in German.—*Translator*).   This explanation, of course, must have appeared somewhat daring even at that time.

Hans was quite guiltless of the many limitations imputed to him concerning his knowledge of symbols. That he was unable to read capitals or Latin script was merely a vagary of the master, like the belief that it was necessary to confine one's self in one's questions to a certain vocabulary and to a certain form. Mr. von Osten's apparent failure to elicit responses from the horse on topics of which it was ignorant is a beautiful illustration of the power of imagination. Mr. von Osten was convinced from the very first that Hans could not answer such questions. When the belief in success was lacking, of course there was not the requisite amount of concentration which, alone, leads to perceptible expressive movements and thus elicits a successful reaction on the part of the horse.

Mr. Schillings, owing to his great impressionability, remained long under the spell of Mr. von Osten's point of view. Thus I find in the record of the September-Commission that the question " How much is 3 plus 2? " was answered incorrectly by Hans, but he responded correctly the moment Mr. Schillings replaced the word " plus " which was " tabooed ", by the word " and ". For a long time also he could receive no response to questions put in French until one day he made the discovery that, curiously enough, the animal never responded adequately unless he himself firmly believed in the possibility of success. It is noteworthy that the Count zu Castell, independently of Mr. Schillings, made the same discovery. Mr. Schillings made his curious discovery—which he was unable to interpret, but which aroused some suspicion—on the following occasion. One day—whether accidentally or because his prejudice was temporarily overcome—he commanded; "Dis deux!". Hans responded promptly with 2 taps. He was greatly surprised and believed that Hans had gotten hold of the French by hearing it spoken in his environment. Possibly he understood also "trois" and "quatre"? He put the questions and received correct responses. He asked again, "dix", "vingt", and so on to "soixante". At "soixante—six" he became doubtful. Indeed, Hans failed him. At "quatre-vingt", the game began again. "Cent", again, succeeded. The old saying that "Faith will move mountains" was verified once more.*

* It has been scientifically proven that a number of supposed mystical phenomena, table-moving, table-rapping, and divination by means of the rod, all are the result of involuntary movements made unawares by those concerned, just as in the case of this work with Hans. (We must of course except those not infrequent instances in which the phenomena in question are purposely and fraudulently simulated.) There is this difference, however, that there the thing affected is a lifeless object,—the table or the rod,—here it is a living organism, the horse; hence there the immediate effect of the movement is physical work in the form of energy expended in moving the table, here the movement becomes a visual stimulus. A number of observations which I find in the relevant literature, and which I shall introduce into this chapter, may serve to show how close is the similarity between the two cases, how much depends upon the questioner, and how little really upon the instrument —whether table or horse—which is acted upon.

Two examples will suffice to illustrate the significance of belief and of the concentrated attention that results from it. The first is taken from the letters of Father P. Lebrun on the divining rod [26], which appeared in 1696. An old woman once told a treasure-seeker that she had always heard that a treasure was buried at a certain place in the fields. The man, who was known as an expert in the art of using the divining rod, immediately set out to locate the gold. Lo, and behold, the moment he set foot on the spot described by the old woman, the branch turns downward, and from its movements the man gathers that twelve feet below ground there lies buried some copper, silver and gold. He calls

Hans's seeming knowledge of the value of coins and cards, of the calendar and the time of day, as well as his ability to recognize persons or their photographs, can now be readily understood. In all of these cases, we had to deal, in so far as knowledge is concerned, only with that of the questioner,—the horse simply tapped the number the questioner had in mind. The meaning which was supposed to be expressed by the tapping never existed as far as Hans was concerned; it was only in the mind of the questioner that the concepts: ace, gold, Sunday, January, were associated with " 1 ", etc. The same was true with regard to all other wonderful feats of memory. The sentence: " Brücke und Weg sind vom

a peasant to dig a pit eleven feet deep, then he sends him away so that no other should get into the secret. He himself digs a foot deeper, but all in vain, for he finds nothing. Standing in the pit, he again takes up the branch. Again it moves, but this time it points upward, as if to indicate that the treasure had disappeared from the earth. Dismayed, he climbs out of the pit and questions the branch a third time. This time it points downward once more. He climbs back into the pit. Presently he feels the prick of conscience (for in the 17th century many regarded the dipping of the divining rod as the work of the Devil). Terrified, he exclaims : " O God, if the thing I am doing here is wrong, then I renounce the Evil One and his rod (s'il y a du mal, je renonce au démon et à la baguette "). Having spoken, he once more takes the rod in hand to test it. It does not move. Horrified, for now there was no longer any doubt that Satan was the cause of its movements, the man makes the sign of the cross and runs away. But he had hardly gone more than two or three hundred paces when the thought strikes him : Is it really true that the branch will no longer move for him ? He throws a coin to the ground, cuts a branch from a bush nearby, and is overjoyed when he notes how it dips down toward the money.

Another example is to be found in a report of the well-known physicist, Ritter [27], of Munich, which appeared during the early part of the 19th century. Ritter, a man with a bent for natural philosophy and metaphysics, describes an instrument which was to replace the divining rod, and which he called " balancier." It was simple enough, consisting

Feinde besetzt ", (The road and the bridge are held by the enemy), which was given to the horse one day and correctly repeated by him on the following day, was not an answer elicited from the horse by means of a question, but rather a system of automatic reactions which were induced by certain involuntary movements of the questioner as stimuli. Far from showing a wonderful memory in these feats—as is claimed for him by the very non-critical compiler, Zell [28]—Hans, on the contrary, has at his service a remarkably small number of associations. For, besides possessing the powers of any ordinary horse, he recognizes only a few meager visual signs. To be sure, we find in the literature a horse that

of a metal strip that was balanced horizontally upon a pivot, and was supposed to be put into motion in the presence of metals. Ritter used this instrument in his numerous experiments with the Italian **Campetti,** a man who had achieved a measure of fame in Europe for his ability to discover springs and metals by the use of the divining rod. Carrying the "balancier" on the tip of the middle finger of his left hand, Campetti—whose integrity one cannot cavil at—had to touch repeatedly a plate of zinc or pewter, and had to count aloud the number of touches he made. The following curious law was found to obtain (that was probably suggested to the subject by Ritter without his being aware of it) : with the first contact the "balancier" turns to the left, with the second to the right, and with the third it remains at rest. At 4 it turns once more to the left, at 5 to the right, at 6 it remains at rest, etc. It remained immovable only at the so-called trigonal numbers (3, 6, 9, 15, 21, etc.). Ritter tells us that when Campetti did not really count or did not think of the number, then it would not have any influence whatever upon the action of the instrument. This Ritter ascribes to the agency of electricity (which in the 18th and 19th centuries was made to play very much the same role that Satan had played in the 16th and 17th centuries).

The similarity of these two cases and that of Mr. Schillings is evident. When the questioner of the horse and the bearers of the "balancier" and of the divining rod are confident of success, they succeed. When they do not expect success, they fail.

was said to have recognized 1500 signals,[29] but all proof is lacking and the report is so meager that we cannot discover whether these signs were auditory or visual.*

Having thus disposed of all questions concerning the horse's apparent feats of reason and memory, let us turn to those in the field of sensation. We shall begin with vision. That Hans was unable to select colored pieces of cloth merely upon the basis of color quality, without reference to their order, was shown in Chapter II. It would, however, be somewhat hasty to infer color-blindness from this fact, as did Romanes [32] on the basis of similar unsucessful responses on the part of a chimpanzee ("Sally" of the London Zoölogical Garden). It is much easier to explain the failure of the horse than that of the monkey on the basis of intellectual poverty, a poverty of associative activity. It presumably can discriminate between the various colors, but it cannot asociate with these their names. The existence of chromatic vision in the lower forms is by no means as unquestionable as is assumed by popular thought. Even teleological considerations which are often brought forward (especially that of the ornamental and protective coloring of so many animals) can never do more than establish a certain probability. For definite proof, we need data given by observation (we have none in this case), or experimental evidence. Such evidence we have, but it is insufficient in quantity and unfortunately most of it was obtained under inadequate experimental

---

* The French investigators Vaschide and Rousseau make a reference to this case, and mistakenly state the number of signals as 1500 instead of 115 [30]. Ettlinger [31] taks over this wrong figure and makes the additional mistake of assuming that the reference is to an original investigation made by the two Frenchmen.

conditions.* We know nothing regarding chromatic vision in the horse, though we have often had trained horses which apparently possessed color discrimination. The earliest report of this kind I find in a work published in the year 1573.³⁶ Here we read that a number of Germans exhibited two horses in Rome which could, upon request of their masters, point out those persons among the spectators who were wearing stockings of any designated color. The passage, " conoscevano i colori ", (they recognized the colors,) proves nothing and no one has ever heard, even in modern times, of a horse that actually knew colors.

Nor did Hans possess anything like that high degree of visual acuity which had been attributed to him. He was supposed to be able to read easily at a distance small, almost illegible script, which we ourselves could decipher only with the greatest difficulty close at hand. It was also supposed that he could distinguish ten- and fifty-

---

* All told, there are hardly more than half dozen experimental investigations of the color-sense in mammals,—to speak only of these. Three of them deserve especial mention. One, the work of the American, Kinnaman, ³³ on two Rhesus monkeys. Then a brief but careful piece of work by Himstedt and Nagel.³⁴ These two investigators were able to determine that their trained poodle could distinguish red of any tone or shade from the other colors, and from Professor Nagel I learned that later the tests were extended and the same was shown to be true concerning the blue and the green. And finally there is an investigation which hitherto has been known only from a reference which Professor Dahl,³⁵ the investigator, himself makes. The work is on a monkey, Cercopithecus (Chlorocebus) griseoviridis Desm. (Professor Dahl has kindly allowed me to look over the records of the experiments. He intends to publish the monograph at an early date.)

All of these investigators arrive at the conclusion that the animals tested by them possess color-sense. The monkey last-mentioned shows one peculiarity : it was unable to distinguish a saturated blue from the black. It will require further tests to clear this up.

pfennig pieces whose faces had become worn beyond recognition for us.   None of these accomplishments have stood the test.   We have no reason to believe that Hans can see the objects about him more clearly than other horses, regarding whom one usually assumes that they receive only vague visual impressions.   Horses do not as a rule seem to be near-sighted as is often asserted by the layman, but rather somewhat far-sighted, or if we may believe Riegel,[37] who tested some six hundred horses, they probably have normal vision.   But we are told that many horses—and according to some authors all —have an innate imperfection which detracts con- siderably from the clarity of vision.   This imperfection consists in an irregular formation of the sclerotic coat and of the lens of the eye.[38]   The two organs do not have the same refraction in all parts.   As a result, objective points are not imaged as points upon the retina.   (Hence the name: astigmatism, i. e., " without points ", for this disorder.)   The retinal image of the object is not only vague, but also distorted.*

Many will doubt whether with such imperfect images an animal can react to directives so minute, as we have asserted to be true in the case of Hans.   In considering this question we must distinguish between the directives for pointing out colors and the directives for tapping and for head movements on the part of the horse.   In point-

* There is no justification for the wide-spread belief that the horse which on account of the greater size of his eye (more correctly, on account of the greater focal distance) receives larger retinal images of objects than does the human eye, for that reason also sees objects, larger than we do.   Horses' shying is often explained in this way.   But the conclusion just mentioned is erroneous.   The retinal image is not the perceptual image.   It undergoes many transformations within the nervous system itself.

ing out and bringing forth pieces of colored cloth there is involved the perception of an object at rest, viz.: the direction of the questioner who is standing quietly; whereas in the case of responses by means of tapping the stimulus is the horse's perception of the questioner's movements. Now, the construction of the horse's eye, as described above, is not favorable for the perception of objects (so-called acuity of vision). This may partly account for the slight success of the horse in those tests in which he was required to select a piece of cloth of a designated color, in so far as these commands were not accompanied by calls or exhortations. Where human observers averaged eighty per cent correct responses (page 135), Hans, under similar conditions was successful in only one-third of the tests. In his errors he was also wider of the mark than were the human observers (page 82). The object perceived, to be sure, is a large one, viz.: the questioner, and he at close range. We must therefore consider more specifically what are the determining factors that make for success or failure of the response. First of all, the innocent questioner very often did not designate the direction with sufficient clearness. Furthermore, Hans presumably was not able to discriminate sufficiently between the direction of the experimenter's eye and that of his head, which two directions did not always coincide. Finally the horse's attention was often diverted, while he was running toward the piece indicated, by the other pieces lying to the right and to the left, and for this reason the addition of a single piece to the otherwise unchanged row of five pieces tended to decrease greatly the chances of success.

The case is different with the perception of the directive signs for tapping, for nodding and shaking the head, etc., all of which require the perception of movements. This is not necessarily more difficult on account of the imperfect constitution of the tissues that serve for the refraction of light. Some authors even aver that this facilitates the perception of moving objects. This view was first advanced by the excellent ophthalmologist, R. Berlin [39] of Stuttgart. In arriving at this view he was guided by the following considerations. The peculiar form of astigmatism of the lens of the horse's eye, which Berlin has described as " butzenscheibenförmig ",* because it appears in the form of a series of glossy concentric circles around the lens nucleus, has the property of enlarging the pathway (and with it the rapidity) of moving retinal images. If we take a speculum by means of which a view may be had of the interior of the eye, and fixate a definite point on the retina of the horse, and then make a slight movement of the head horizontally, we find that the point fixated moves—apparently at least— toward the border of the pupil. In a normally constructed eye this seeming movement will be in a straight line, while in the eye of the horse, (according to Berlin), its path is curved, and therefore longer. Berlin believes that the same thing which here occurs in the case of this merely apparent movement, must also happen when an external moving object is imaged on the horse's retina. Its pathway, too, will be curved, and therefore longer, so that if the head of Mr. von Osten moves past the animal's eye, then the image on the horse's retina will take a longer, more circuitous route than it would if the eye

---

* " Butzenscheiben " are the small circular panes of green glass, used in leaded windows in early days. They are high in the middle (hence the name : " Butze," a protuberance) with a number of concentric circles around the central elevation.—Translator.

were not astigmatic. We cannot, however, immediately conclude from the fact that an objective movement is imaged as being greater in extent on the retina, that it will therefore be more readily perceived by much less that it will appear greater to, the horse, than would be the case if the lens were normally constructed. The visual percept is not immediately dependent upon the retinal processes, for between the two are interpolated complex, inaccessible nervous processes. Still, Berlin believes that he is justified in drawing this conclusion from a number of relevant considerations. Accepting it, he believes that it would be possible for the horse to perceive movements, that for the human eye, which is not subject to this form of astigmatism, would lie below the threshold.

This theory, the simplicity of which certainly must make a strong appeal, has been adopted by a number of well-known investigators (Schleich [40], Königshöfer [41]). If we also could accept it, then Hans's phenomenal power of perceiving the movements of objects would be explained. But doubts arise which restrain us. Even if we were to accept Berlin's view in general, we should still come upon the following difficulties. In the first place, it is questionable whether the peculiar form of astigmatism mentioned is indeed as common as he supposes.* The references in the literature are exceedingly

---

* Since no opportunity was given us to examine Hans's eyes we do not know what their condition is in this respect. Though it would have been interesting to know, it would hardly make any difference in the views presented. If Hans should prove to be either far or near-sighted, then, if we are to make any supposition at all, it would be that the defect could not be very great, since near sightedness exceeding 2 or 3 diopters and far-sightedness exceeding one diopter is seldom found in the case of the horse. According to Mr. von Osten, Hans at one time manifested

meager on this point. In order to make a few tests at least, I undertook to examine nine horses with the aid of Dr. R. Simon, oculist, to whom I am greatly beholden for the assistance given in these and other tests to be mentioned presently. In not one of the nine cases did we discover anything like the curved deflection which is supposed to be the sign of the form of astigmatism in question. But in order to test objectively whether Berlin's assumption were justified, we examined in the laboratory fresh specimens taken from two horses. The eyes were fastened in a frame in what corresponded to their normal position. Their posterior spherical wall (i. e., their respective retinal surface) was replaced by a piece of ground glass. On a spherical surface linear movements of a point of light are always imaged as curves, no matter what the shape of the lens forming the image may be. (For a more detailed statement see page 170, at close of note.) Since, however, our investigation had to do only with those curves which were due to the qualities peculiar to the lens, we had to replace the spherical by a plane projection surface. In front of the eye thus modified a strong light was placed at such a distance that the image of it, produced on the improvised back of the eye by the cornea and the lens, was a sharply defined point of light. Now, when the source of light was moved, the point of light would also move on the glass plate. Sitting at some distance behind the eye, we observed the movements of this point through a telescope. Thus we became witnesses of what happens upon the horse's retina when a moving object passes in

a tendency to shy easily. Be this as it may, for little could be concluded from it, since in many extremely shy horses, no kind of visual imperfection can be discovered.

front of his eye. Although we saw the point of light move through relatively long distances both horizontally and vertically, no sort of deflection in its pathway could be noted. Berlin's exposition does not hold true for the eyes of the horses, either living or dead, which were examined by us.

But in the case of some of the horses in whom Berlin had seen the phenomenon for which we sought in vain, he himself tells us, the deflection was very slight. In that case, it would appear, no great advantage would be gained along the lines indicated. But even assuming the degree of deflection to be very great, his theory goes to pieces on the very point it was supposed to explain. A concrete example will make this clear. If Mr. von Osten, standing two feet away from the horse, raised his head $\frac{1}{5}$ millimeter (which figure by no means represents the extreme values that were obtained), then in the horse's retinal image every point of the man's head would move through a distance of 0.0025 millimeter—assuming the horse's eye to be free from astigmatism and assuming its focal distance to be 25.5 millimeters. If, however, other conditions remaining the same, we presuppose an extreme form of astigmatism, one in which the path of the retinal image is not a straight line, but is deflected into a semicircle, then each point would pass through a distance of nearly 0.004 millimeter. If the sensitive retinal elements have a diameter of 0.002 millimeter (as Berlin, somewhat inexactly, states), then from two to four elements would be stimulated in case there were no astigmatic deflection. But in case the deflection did take place, it would not necessarily involve more elements, as can be seen by making a simple graph; indeed we can imagine cases in which the circuitous path would involve even fewer elements than the straight one. And finally, when the movement which the horse is to perceive, does not occur in a straight line but in the form of a curve, (which will generally be the rule), then the astigmatism will tend in many cases to decrease the curvature of the image's path on the retina, and sometimes even obviate it entirely. In all these cases, on Berlin's own theory, the perception of the movements would be hindered rather than aided.*

* For the benefit of specialists I would say the following in addition to the more general remarks just made. For the most part, the determinations of refraction made on the eye of the horse are still rather unreliable. In sciascopy there is a dispute among investigators concerning ambiguous shadows, and in the use of the refraction-ophthalmoscope no definite region of the eye's background has been adhered to by the various investigators. It appears that Riegel, whose diligent researches mentioned on page 164 were published in 1904, knew nothing concerning the round area in the horse's eye, discovered by I. Zürn [42] in 1902. Also, if so great a degree of astigmatism is really the rule as is emphasized especially by Hirschberg [43] and Berlin,[44] then the simple refractive index usually given—sometimes within a half diopter—would be meaningless. Berlin [45] and Bayer [46] believe the vagueness of the retinal image resulting from the astigmatism, is offset by this : that the oval pupil functions as a stenopaic slit. In view of the width of the horse's pupil this appears to me to be rather hypothetical.

Concerning Berlin's theory of deflecting astigmatism I would say the following : Of the two ophthalmoscopic signs mentioned as being characteristic of this form of astigmatism,—the concentric circles and the arcuate deflection of the pathway of the fixated points,—when there is a movement of the eye of the observer (or of the eye observed), according to Berlin the former is not so constant as the latter. So far as I know, the concentric ring formation is mentioned only by Bayer [47] and Riegel,[48] and is said to occur principally in horses with myopic vision— and hence, relatively, in a minority of cases. Judging from the particulars, we are inclined to believe that a case of " Butzenscheiben "—lens reported by Schwendimann [48a] is in reality a case of senile sclerosis. Berlin repeatedly warns us against mistaking the one for the other.[48b] The arcuate deflection, on the other hand, has not been mentioned else-

But to come now to the most pertinent objection. We saw that Berlin's whole train of thought rested upon the

where as a personal observation. In Berlin's calculation [49] of the increase in the extent of the retinal pathway an ambiguity has crept in. He says that "in the astigmatic eye there are stimulated 207 times as many nervous elements as would be stimulated in the ideally normal eye." It ought to read "207 more" instead of "207 times as many." And this number holds only for the one case computed by Berlin, and under the specific assumption that exactly $\frac{\pi}{2}$ times the normal number of elements were stimulated (571 instead of 364). Therefore the general statement which Bayer [50] makes in his text-book, that according to Berlin's evaluation "207 times more nervous elements" are stimulated in the astigmatic eye than in the non-astigmatic one, does not hold true.

Closing this note, a few remarks concerning the experiments made by Dr. Simon and myself. All of the nine horses were tested for the vertical image by means of the ophthalmoscope. In most cases Wolff's electric speculum was used. Atropine was not employed.—— For the laboratory tests the adipose and the muscular tissues were removed from the eye-ball and the rear part of the bulb cut away. The front part, containing the cornea and the lens, was fastened over one opening of a metal cylinder which was closed at the other end by means of a disc of ground glass. The whole, approximately as long as a horse's eye, was filled with a normal salt solution whose refractive index (1.336) corresponds quite closely with that of the vitreous humor of the horse's eye. The pressure from within was regulated so that on the one hand it was not dimmed and yet on the other there were no wrinkles in the cornea. The source of light——the filament of a Nernst lamp——was moved about in a plane 120 cm. distant from the eye and perpendicular to the optic axis. It was moved through the point of intersection as well as at various distances from it. Movement in horizontal and vertical directions was in each case along lines 150 centimeters in length, which would correspond to an angle of vision of not less than 64°. The pathway of the imaged point was controlled by means of the cross-hairs of the telescope. If in the same way we observe through the sclerotic of an intact eye-bulb a point of light falling upon the retina and shining through the sclerotic and choroid (which is not difficult when we use an intense light), then to the observer its pathway will, of course, appear to be deflected convexly toward the periphery,—and the deflection will appear the greater, the farther the point of light is removed from the optic axis.

assertion that it made no difference whether we regarded by means of the speculum the seeming movement of a fixed retinal point, or whether the image of an external moving object is passing over the horse's retina. As a matter of fact, however, these two processes are very different from one another. In moving the mirror, with its small opening we are looking through ever changing portions of the horse's lens,—testing it out, as it were. The horse, on the other hand, sees with all parts of the lens simultaneously, in so far as the lens is not covered by the iris. The arcuate deflection, which is nothing but a registration of the difference in the indices of refraction of the different parts of the lens used consecutively, might thus be formed for the observer using the mirror, but never for the horse. For these reasons we cannot conclude that the kind of astigmatism described can really increase the horse's acuity in the perception of movements.

Since the light-refracting apparatus of the horse's eye does not offer a satisfactory explanation for the extraordinary keenness of visual perception possessed by the Osten horse, we must go a step further and ask whether it may not perhaps be found in the part immediately sensitive to light, the retina. That portion really would seem to be adapted to the perception of movements of minimal extent, and for this reason: it is more than three times as great in extent as the human retina, and the horse's retinal images are likewise larger owing to the position of the nodal point. The cells of the retina that are sensitive to light, the rods and cones, might therefore be correspondingly larger than those of the human eye, without thereby making the whole organ less efficient than the human eye. But the most recent measurements [51] have shown that the rods and cones of the horse's eye are more minute than ours. Assuming that, in the case of the horse, as is presumably the case in human vision, the transition of a stimulus from one retinal cell to the next already in itself induces a sensation of movement, then the horse ought indeed be extraordinarily keen in the perception of moving objects (provided that the horse's more minute cells are packed just as closely as in the human retina). And besides, there are two specially adapted areas within the retina of the horse. The " band " (streifenförmige Area ") which was discovered fifteen years ago by Chievitz,[52] is a strip of 1 to 1½ millimeters in width, traversing the entire retina horizontally, and is noteworthy on account of its structure and probably, too, on account of its greater efficiency. It may have something to do with the accomplishments of the Osten horse; but in how far it would be hard to say. The other noteworthy portion of the horse's retina is the " round area " discovered some four years ago, located at the rear outer end of the " band ", and it is the best-equipped part of the horse's retina and corresponds to the area of clearest vision, the yellow spot, in the human eye. But this round area need not come in for consideration by us, for its location would indicate that it is used in binocular vision, that is, seeing with both eyes.[53] But in all our experiments the Osten horse observed only with one eye. That does not mean, however, that under other circumstances the round area may not be of very great importance.

In the present state of our knowledge, all attempts at explanation are, of course, of the nature of hypotheses. If further investigations should disclose this explanation to be untenable, then we would either have to suppose some unknown power in the eye of the horse,* or else seek a cause in the animal's brain. Further experiments on other horses would be necessary in order to discover whether the species as a whole possesses this ability or whether only certain ones are thus endowed. The former is of course more probable. In this particular case conditions were unusually favorable for the develop-

* Königshöfer, who as we have already said, seconds the explanation given by the ophthalmologist Berlin (and who confounds "Butzen-scheiben" astigmatism with the common, so-called regular form), believes [54] that not only astigmatism but also the shape of the blind-spot of the eye must be taken into consideration. This portion of the retina, where the fibres of the optic nerve enter the eye (and called "blind-spot" because there are no cells there that are sensitive to light) is very nearly circular in man, but differs in shape in the different species of animals. Königshöfer thought he had discovered that a relatively elongated blind spot was favorable to keenness of vision. If we place the mammalia in series on the basis of their relative keenness of vision, he says, we would find that this series is identical with the one in which they are grouped with reference to the form of the blind-spot from the circular up to the most elongated. (In such a series the marmot takes the place of honor.)

This exposition is not very satisfactury, however. We cannot be sure what he means by "keenness of vision" ("scharfäugigkeit"). Is it visual acuity in the usual sense of the term (as is said in one of his passages), or keenness in the perception of the movements of objects, (this would appear to be his real meaning), or both at the same time. But whatever the significance he may put into the term, any such attempt at grouping the lower forms must prove unsatisfactory from the very start on account of the scant data which we possess on visual perception in animals. The experiences of the hunt upon which Königshöfer partly bases his view, are entirely inadequate for such a purpose. This much is certain, that the Osten horse, in spite of a blind-spot which, thought somewhat oval, is by no means very elongated, possesses an extraordinary acuity in the perception of movements. Even if the parallelism mentioned by Königshöfer were really shown to exist, it would not explain the matter until it were also shown in what way keenness of vision is dependent upon the shape of the blind-spot,—a portion of the eye which is not immediately operative in the visual sensation at all.

ment of this ability. We must bear in mind that in all probability Mr. von Osten's movements very gradually became as minute as they are now, and that therefore Hans at first learned to react to such as were relatively coarse. Furthermore, his practice extended throughout four years and during this time it was his sole occupation. Without specific predisposition, however, all this practice would have been utterly futile. We can also readily appreciate how indispensable in the struggle for existence a well-developed power of perceiving moving objects must be to horses (and most other animals) living in their natural condition and habitat, in order to be aware of the approach of enemies, or, in the case of carnivora, the presence of prey. In view of all these considerations we can readily see how it was possible that the horse, perhaps in spite of rather defective vision, could react with precision to movement-stimuli which escaped observation by human eyes.

We can understand also the horse's never-flagging attentiveness when we recall that self-preservation prompts eternal vigilance over against all that is going on in the animal's environment. (In the case of Hans, hunger was at first the motive; later, habit did the work.) Furthermore, the lower form is not hindered in giving itself over to its sense-impressions by the play of abstract thought which tends so strongly to direct inward our psychic energy,—at least, in the case of the cultured.

Nevertheless, Hans still remains a phenomenon not only in excelling all his critics in the power of observation, but also in that he is the first of his species, in fact the first animal, in which this extraordinary perceptual power has been proven experimentally to be present. It has long been known [55] that horses could be trained to

respond to cues in the form of slight movements, which
remained unnoticed by the layman, and this fact has
been made use of by circus trainers to its fullest extent.
But such signs, I have discovered, are without exception, of a far coarser sort than those we have here described, and they can be instantly detected by the practised observer. Nor was it known to professional trainers
that it was possible for the master to direct a horse to
any point of the compass simply by means of the quiet
posture of the body. For this reason it was believed
that no signs could possibly be involved in the color-
selecting-tests (cf. Supplement III, page 255). In this
we have the support of some of our experts, as is witnessed by the following extract from a letter of his Ex-
cellency Count G. Lehndorff, one of our best hippological
authorities, who at one time carefully examined the Osten
horse. (The letter was addressed to Mr. Schillings, and
I have permission of both gentlemen to use it). In it he
says: " If the author's statements, in which you also have
concurred, are correct, and if, as a matter of fact, the
horse really does react to such minute movements as are
absolutely imperceptible to the human observer, then we
have indeed something quite new, for hitherto no one
would have believed that horses can perceive movements
which man cannot. But I am even more surprised by the
explanation of the color-selecting feats.— This too, is
something absolutely new. One would not have deemed
it possible that a horse could do anything of the kind
simply by using the posture of a man's body as a cue to
which it could react with such precision."

And yet, even though both facts were new concerning
the horse and had not hitherto been proven experimentally regarding any other species, nevertheless something

of this sort has been known concerning the dog for some time.   His ability to single out an object upon which his master had intently fixed his gaze, was made the basis of a special form of training, called " eye-training," [56] nearly one hundred years ago.   The dog was taught to focus constantly upon his master's eyes and then upon command to select the object which he, the master, had been fixating.   Such a dog has been described by the naturalists A. and K. Müller.[57]   But the master of the dog, unlike Mr. von Osten, would not permit anyone else to work with the animal, and the two brothers, recognizing the trick, were justified in adding that " the whole affair aimed at deceiving the public, and the dog's reputation was but a means of making money ".   The success of such exhibitions appeared furthermore, to depend upon the close proximity of the trainer and the dog, whereas the direction of the head (and even of the body) could very probably be perceived at greater distances also. At least we learn from a reputable source that in the hunt, dogs can perceive from the mere posture of their master, what direction he intends to take.[58]

But a still more curious fact is this, that dogs, too, learn —evidently spontaneously—to react to the minimal involuntary expressive movements of their master.   The first example mentioned in the literature on the subject is that of an English bull-dog called Kepler, belonging to the English astrophysicist, Sir William Huggins.[59] We are told that this dog seemingly could solve the most difficult problems, such as extracting square roots and the like.   The numbers were indicated by barking,— thus one bark was for one, two barks for two, etc.   Every correct solution was rewarded with a piece of cake. Huggins states explicitly that he gave no signals volun-

tarily, but that he was convinced that the dog could see
from the questioner's face, when he must cease barking,
for he would never for an instant divert his gaze during
the process. Huggins was unable, however, to discover
the nature of the effective signs. This satisfactory,
though still unproven, explanation has been accepted by
specialists, among them Sir John Lubbock.[60]   I, too,
regard this dog as a predecessor of our Hans.

A similar case is reported by Mr. Hugo Kretschmer,
a writer of Breslau, in the " Schlesische Zeitung " of
August 21, 1904. To him I am beholden for a detailed
written statement, which he has kindly permitted me to
use in this connection. The gentleman named, first
trained his dog to ring the table-bell, and this, by pressing the dog's paw upon the bell-button. When the dog
had learned to do this independently, his master tried to
teach him the rudiments of numbers, in such a way that
the animal was to give one ring of the bell for the number 1, two for 2, etc. But these attempts failed utterly
and had to be abandoned. But Mr. Kretschmer had
noticed that he was able to get the dog to ring any number which he, Mr. Kretchmer, might decide upon.
(Success was always rewarded by a bit of bread and
butter.) At first Mr. Kretschmer tried to imagine vividly
only the final number, but failed thereby to elicit correct
responses from the dog. But he did succeed when he tried
making a series of separate volitions. Thus for the number 5, he would " will " each separate push of the button
on the part of the dog. Even so, however, he never got
beyond 9, for then the dog would become impatient and
would ring the bell continuously. Anything that diverted
the dog's attention, such as noises, etc., also entailed
failure. In these tests master and dog had faced each

other, each gazing steadfastly at the other.   Mr. Kretchmer was convinced, however, that the dog was not
guided by any sort of sign, but rather by suggestion.
He based his belief on the following two observations.
After some practice, he says, the tests were also successful when he did not look at the dog, but stood back to
back with it, or when he screened himself from the dog's
view by stepping to one side behind a curtain.   The
tests were unsuccessful, on the other hand, whenever he
was mentally fatigued or had taken some alcoholic drink.
The arguments do not appear to me to be adequate.   If
he turned his back upon the dog and no other observer
was present, he had no means of knowing whether the
dog did not, after all, peer around to get a peep at him.
If others who knew the desired number, were present,
the dog might have gotten his cues from them.   And
there may be some doubt whether the curtain adequately
served the purpose for which it was intended.   At any
rate, it was added that all attempts to influence the dog
from an adjoining room—which would thus exclude
effectively all visual signs—were utter failures.   I am
also strengthened rather than weakened in my belief, by
the second argument which Mr. Kretschmer makes, viz.:
that mental fatigue or the use of alcohol on the part of
the questioner tends to make the result unsatisfactory.
We noted a similar effect in the case of the horse (page
150), where a disturbance of the " rapport " between the
questioner and the horse was invoked by some by way of
explantion.   The facts were explained by us much more
simply.   We attributed the result to the close correlation
between the type of mental concentration and the nature
of the expressive movements—a correlation which we
have shown experimentally to exist.   I cannot, therefore,

subscribe to the view that this dog did not require either visual or other sensory signs. The tests which were made for the purpose of strengthening that view, are on a par, I believe, with those mentioned on page 45. And since auditory, olfactory, and other stimuli, though not impossible, still are improbable, I believe that our Hans, Huggins's dog, and the one belonging to Mr. Kretschmer, differ from one another only in this, that the first taps, the second barks, and the third presses a bell-button.

And finally I have access to a letter from the Rhine Province in which there is a brief account of a dog that would promptly obey any command that was given without a sound and supposedly without the accompaniment of the slightest kind of gesture. It is specially mentioned that the animal steadily watched its master during these tests. The perception of the slightest involuntary expressive movements is in all probability the secret in this case also. Here, too, suggestion has been invoked by way of explanation, but there was not the slightest attempt made to find for it a more specific foundation, and we cannot suppress an objection based on the matter of principle. It is incumbent upon anyone who uses a term so ambiguous, to define what content he desires to have put into it. If he does not do this, he is giving us, instead of a concept, a bare word, instead of bread, a stone.

While we must reject the explanation based on suggestion,* we believe, on the other hand, that we have

---

* I can find examples of supposed suggestion in the case of animals given only by Rouhet.[61] He says that by means of suggestion he taught a half-year old half-blooded mare-colt which he had raised himself, to fetch and carry, and this in a very short time. In order to indicate to here again, evidence of the presence of visual signs, given unwittingly and involuntarily, just as I am sure that they were involved in the two preceding cases, and similarly in the case of the Huggins dog. Since the effective signs were discoverable in none of these canine predecessors of Hans, an investigation would be desirable, based upon the insight gained as a result of these experiments upon Mr. von Osten's horse. Unfortunately this is impossible, since the dogs in question are dead. But others like them undoubtedly exist in many places. We might mention that when Hans first came under the limelight of public attention, there was also frequent reference to the Huggins dog, but he soon dropped out

the colt what was wanted, Rouhet would concentrate with his whole mind upon the object intended (a watch), and at the same time he would bend forward slightly. In the third test, that is at the end of fifteen minutes, he had accomplished his purpose, and in the tenth lesson, no more mistakes occurred. The colt would fail to respond, however, as soon as he refrained from making any gestures, or was in a laissez faire frame of mind, or when he thought of other things. He therefore believes that there must have been some kind of immediate, though inexplicable, connection between the brain of the trainer and that of the horse. I think the explanation is evident : the connection was not as he thought, an immediate one, but arising through the mediation of the man's attitude (" attitude un peu baissée "), and of his movements (" gestes "), both resulting from his intense concentration (" tension de la pensée ").

In general we may say that, no matter what content we may wish to put into the term " suggestion," not a single fact has since come to light which would justify, and much less demand, the application of the term to lower forms, unless we would expand the definition of the term to the extent of comprising every kind of command, every arousal of ideas, whatsoever. But it would then be nothing but a new name for old knowledge [62] and would lose all explanatory value. (Hypnotism, so-called, in the case of horses, I shall discuss elsewhere in another connection.)

of the discussion again.[63] And this for two reasons. The dog never took his gaze from his master and appeared to be entirely dependent upon him in his reactions. Hans, on the other hand, seemed to give evidence of a high degree of independence and never appeared to look at the questioner. But we know now that, though he was never dependent upon the will of his master, he, too, abjectly hung upon the man's involuntary movements and never for a moment lost him from view. But since the horse is able to observe with one eye alone, and needed to direct only it and not the entire head toward the questioner, in order to focus comfortably, one could not conclude as to his line of vision from the direction of the head. Since, furthermore, in the horse the pupil is hardly distinguishable from the darkly pigmented iris and since the white sclerotic is hidden by the eyelids, except when the eye is turned very much, it is difficult to determine what direction the eye is taking. I once purposely stepped backward to the horse's flank, so that he had to turn his eye far back and thus the outer border of the iris and the white sclerotic coat became visible and all doubt concerning the line of vision was removed. This doubt could never arise in the case of the dog, the median plane of whose head is always directed toward the object fixated, and Zborzill is justified in saying, as he does, in his discussion of training of the kind mentioned on page 177, " But any careful observer can immediately guess the manner in which such a dog has been trained." [64] If Hans had chanced to possess so-called " glass-eyes "—in which the dark pigment is wholly or partly lacking, so that the black pupil is clearly defined against the lighter background,—then no doubt could ever have arisen concerning the direction of the eye, and Hans never would have come to be regarded as the " clever " Hans.

After the publication of the December report, Hans acquired a reputation for excellence in thought-reading and thus the discussion of thought-reading among animals in general became once more the order of the day. That is to say that many of our domestic animals are—like the human mind-reader (à la Cumberland), —supposed to have the ability to infer the thoughts of their masters from slight involuntary movements. They are thus aware when the feeding hour approaches, when they may go out in the open, etc. They also appear to be aware that their welfare lies in our hands, and therefore would seem to have a vital interest in divining our intentions and our wishes. Not only our spoken words, but also numberless movements—usually without our knowing it and often contrary to our desire—speak a clear language. As is well said by the American neuropathologist, Beard, [65] (who first explained the phenomenon of thought-reading, on the basis of the perception of very minute muscular jerks, and therefore called it " muscle-reading " or " body-reading ") : " Every horse that is good for anything is a muscle-reader; he reads the mind of his driver through the pressure on the bit,— though not a word of command is uttered." We know that in the case of perfectly trained horses the rider's mere thought of the movement which he expects the horse to make, is seemingly sufficient to cause the animal to execute it.* Such cases are of course very much like

* An illustration is given by Babinet [66] concerning the horse of an English lord. Mr. Burkhardt-Foottit, also, that excellent trainer, who has been master for more than forty of the most highly-trained horses, tells us that while sitting on a well-managed horse it sometimes hap-

that of our Hans, excepting that instead of visual signs they involve aids of a mechanical nature, which, however, does not alter the general principle, since both of them are of the nature of sensory stimulation. But we must not overlook the essential difference between this so-called thought-reading on the part of animals and that which is done by man. The human thought-reader can interpret movements, for he is familiar with the ideas which are their source. Thus when at the second tap, I notice a very slight jerk of the subject's head, and a stronger one at the fifth tap, I infer that he thought of the problem $2 + 3 = 5$. While the experimenter thus cannot be said to read thoughts, he still infers them. The animal, on the other hand, we may be reasonably sure, draws no such inferences. In its conscious life it remains ever on the sensory level. If we could ask Hans about it, he would

pened that he had merely thought of making a certain turn, when the horse immediately executed it, before he, the rider, had to his knowledge given any sign or aid. An observation belonging under this head is also made in Tolstoi's "Anna Karenina"[67], this perfect mine of acute psychological observation. In the famous description of the race we are told concerning Count Wronskij riding his Frou-Frou just behind Machotin mounted upon Gladiator, who was leading the race : " At the very moment when Wronskij thought that it was time to overtake Machotin, Frou-Frou, divining her master's thought, increased her pace considerably and this without any incitement on his part. She began to come nearer to Gladiator from the more favorable, the near side. But Machotin would not give it up. Wronskij was just considering that he might get past by making the larger circuit on the off-side, when Frou-Frou was already changing direction and began to pass Gladiator on that side." Similar experiences might be gathered elsewhere. Not infrequently the reflection of the rider that his horse had not for a long time indulged in some trick peculiar to him, will immediately call it forth ; or doubts on the part of the rider concerning the possibility of crossing some barrier, are often the cause of the horse's fall or of his refusal to leap and of his running away.

probably answer: " As soon as my master stoops forward,
I begin to tap; as soon as he moves, I stop.   The thing
which induces me to act thus is the carrot which is given
me; what it is that induces my master to make his movements, I do not know."—It is therefore erroneous to
believe that animals require the power of abstract thinking in order to utilize the signs which are consciously
or unconsciously given them, as is argued by Goldbeck [68]
when he says with reference to the training for visual
signs, which we have already mentioned before:
" There the dog has consciously interpreted the visual
impression in terms of the conclusion that he is expected
to bring forth the leaf indicated."   Nor was there any
justification for the critic who thought he could put the
essence of the report of December, given in Supplement
IV, into the following words: " He (Hans) showed that
he has the power of attention, can draw logical conclusions, and can communicate the result of his thinking,—
and all this independently."   Yet none of this had been
asserted.   The whole thing may be explained satisfactorily
by means of a process of simple association established
between the signs observed in the master and certain reactions on the part of the horse.   The fact that the movements made were so exquisitely minute does not change
the matter in the least.   Such signs call for a high degree
of sensory keenness and great concentration of attention,
but by no means an " extremely high intelligence."

Let us turn now from the consideration of visual perception to that of auditory perception in the horse.   We
saw that the fact that Hans was able to respond to commands which were only inwardly enunciated, that is,
commands which were merely thought of but not spoken,
was not proof of great acuity of hearing, but rather that

hearing was not at all involved. If Hans had been deaf he would, none the less, have promptly obeyed the commands. Blind and near-sighted horses try to overcome their deficiency by means of the sense of hearing, and hence show a pronounced play of ears. In the case of the Osten horse, however, attention has been diverted from auditory stimuli in the process of habituation to visual signs, and as a result ear-movements are almost completely wanting. One is not of course permitted to deny *a priori* that perhaps some associations might have been formed between objects and the vocal signs belonging to them, e. g., between the colored cloths and the names of the colors if both had been presented together oftener than was the case.

But there is a dearth of reliable observation as to how far auditory associations of this sort may be established in horses. Usually the following is cited. Horses learn to start off, to stop, and to turn about in response to calls. They are able to distinguish properly between the expressions " right " and " left ", or equivalent terms. Upon command they will start to walk, to trot or to run. And they also know the name by which they are usually called. All authors agree that cavalry horses understand the common military commands; one writer even avers that they excel the recruits in this respect.[69] Some believe that in riding schools the horses pay closer heed to the calls of the riding-master than to the control of unpractised riders, even when the two are at variance with one another.[70] My experience with the Osten horse and a number of other pertinent observations aroused in me the suspicion that much that is called or spoken in the process of managing a horse may possibly be just so much labor lost. In consequence I made a series of relevant experiments. I have thus far tested twenty-five horses of different kinds, from the imported Arabian and English full-blood, down to the heavy draft-horse. The experiments were made partly in the courtyard of military barracks, partly in the circus, and partly in a riding-school or in private stalls. I am specially indebted for kind assistance to Messrs. von Lucanus, Busch, and to H. H. Burkhardt-Foottit and E. Schumann, the two excellent trainers connected with the Busch Circus. During these tests, the horses were always amid circumstances familiar to them, whether free or bridled, under a rider or hitched to a wagon. All aids or signals, except the calls, were eliminated in so far as it was possible.

The results of those tests were in substance as follows: Many horses react to a smack of the lips by a rather fast trot. Many stop on the cry " Hola " or " Brr ". This last was nicely illustrated in the case of two carriage horses supplied with large blinders and held with a loose rein, and hitched to a landau. One of them regularly stopped when the " brr " was given by the driver, whereas the other, which had not been habituated to this signal, kept serenely on the trot, so that the vehicle regularly veered off the track—a sure sign that no unintentional aid was being given by means of the reins. Other horses, again, were accustomed to halt in response to a long-drawn-out " hola ", but it was the cadence of melody rather than the word that was effective, since any other word, or even a series of inarticulate sounds, would produce the same result, provided they were given with the proper inflection. When this was changed, then the response would fail.

The result was not so apparent when it came to controlling the kinds of gait. One riding-school horse, when

lunged and in a gallop, could be induced by a friendly
call—the word again was a matter of inconsequence—to
slacken his pace into a trot and from a trot into a walk.
But this reaction was by no means very precise. Another
a full-blood, contrary to the trainer's expectation and to
his great astonishment, failed to respond to any kind of
spoken command as soon as the one who carried the
reins refrained from making any movements which might
indicate what was wanted. (To refrain from all expressive movements of this kind is by no means an easy
matter). The slightest move, apart from any help by
means of the reins or the whip-handle, was sufficient to
evoke a response. The results in the case of the military
horses, differed in many particulars. Thanks to the
courtesy of Captain von Lucanus I had the opportunity
of testing three cavalry horses, two geldings and one
mare, aged nine, thirteen, and nineteen years respectively,
and all of them in the regiment ever since their fourth
year. They had been selected as the " most intelligent "
in the squadron, and we were assured that they would
obey punctiliously all the usual commands. They were
ranged behind one another, with the customary distance
of two horses' lengths between, and were ridden each by
his accustomed rider. Both starting and stopping upon
command were tested. The horses were held by the
reins, but the riders were cautioned to refrain from giving
any aid that might cause the horse to start when starting
was to be tested, or that might restrain him when stopping in response to the spoken command was to be tested.
If a suspicion arose—a thing which happened only twice,
however—that a rider had actively aided in his horse's
reaction, then an officer would mount into the saddle.
If it appeared that one of the horses was simply imitat-

ing the others, then the others were purposely restrained by their respective riders. The commands were given by the corporal who usually had charge of the horses. In a few cases the sergeant of the squadron gave the commands, but this made no difference in the success of the experiment. Now as to the results. Whenever the horses were trotting or walking, all commands, without exception, were in vain. They effected neither an increase nor a decrease in the pace. A result was obtained only when the horses were standing when the test began; and this result was simple enough,—upon certain calls the animals would respond by beginning to walk. This was the only reaction that was obtained. The most effective of the commands appeared to be "Squadron,—march!" But the command "Squadron!" or "March!" alone, were quite as effective; yet none of these commands was obeyed without exception. Reactions were occasionally obtained in response to "trot!", "gallop!" "retreat!", (the usual introductory "squadron" was purposely omitted here, because it alone sufficed to start the horses). But the reactions were always the same, viz., to start on a walk. Another series of commands (such as those which are addressed to the rider alone, e. g., "Lances down!") had no effect whatever; a certain amount of selection therefore did seem to take place. In all these tests the order of the horses with reference to each other's position was repeatedly changed. One of the horses, the youngest, and reputed to be the most "intelligent", (he was as a matter of fact the most spirited), gave evidence of a gregarious instinct, intensified by habit, which, if it had been overlooked, might have become a source of serious error. Not being accustomed to go at the head, when so placed it started properly in only 18% of all such cases. When, however, (other conditions remaining the same,) he was put in second or third place, he started properly in 67% of the tests, and if we take into account only those cases in which the three most effective commands were used (" Squadron ! ", " March ! ", and " Squadron—march ! ") he reacted correctly in 91% of the cases. (The number of tests was 17, 36 and 22 respectively for the three groups mentioned.)   The horse, therefore, almost always began to step properly when he stood behind one of his companions, but seldom when he stood at the head.   And when he stood at the head and began to walk at the proper moment, it was plain that it was a case of imitation and not initiative, for the horse was still able to see the others, owing to the extent of his field of vision backward, and he was always the last to move, whereas otherwise he was always the first to move, and always difficult to restrain.   So when the horses to the rear were restrained or when the intervening distance of two horses' lengths was lessened, so that this gelding could not see the one in the rear, he failed completely to respond.   Accordingly these three horses did little to justify the faith which their squadron had placed in them.

Now a few words on the manner in which horses react upon the call of their names.   We are not concerned with those that are seldom or never called by name (such as those in the cavalry).   I have not discovered one horse that constantly and unequivocally reacted upon the mention of its name (though I would not assert that there are none that would do so.)   I was nearly always able to convince the owners or grooms, who at first had maintained a contrary opinion, that any inarticulate sound was capable of producing the same effect as the calling of the name. What the significance of inflection may be, I am not at all certain. When a certain one of a number of horses standing in the same stable was called, all of them responded by pricking their ears, raising their heads, or else turning about. For this reason the reaction of the horse specifically called lost all significance. Likewise the call which is ordinarily used in lunging when the man in the center of the circle wishes the horse to change its gait, or to advance toward him, also proved ineffectual as soon as the man inhibited every sort of movement. A slight nod, on the other hand, was always effective. Several times I have tried to call horses to me, when they were free and running about in the arena, but was unsuccessful. After I had given them some sugar, however, they would always come to me—whether I had called or not—and would then refuse to leave my side. But this is a matter of common observation.

I would, however, regard all of these tests as merely provisional. In spite of the greatest effort, it was not always possible to control all the conditions of the experiment, and furthermore, the number of tests would have to be materially increased in order to yield an appreciation of the difference due to race, age, and the individual variation and training of horses. But we may, even now, be sure of one thing. Over against the certainty with which horses react to visual stimuli (in the form of movements perceived), it does not appear that the formation of auditory associations is greatly favored by nature in these animals,—indeed, auditory associations are far less common than is generally supposed.* Horses compare very unfavorably with dogs in

* All the authors who have given practical suggestions for the training of horses, whether free or with lunging reins, have great faith in

this respect.   The latter easily learn to react with a high
degree of precision to auditory signs,—as I learned from
a series of experiments which I was enabled to perform.
The Osten horse, therefore, does not stand alone among
his kind in his inferior auditory equipment, as one might
be tempted to believe at first blush.

the efficacy of calls, but usually recommend a mingling of calls and
movements in the way of signs, (thus Loiset,[71] Baucher,[72] von Arnim[63]).
It therefore cannot be stated just in how far the calls really effect anything.   In other cases I am inclined to doubt outright the influence
which is ascribed to the auditory signs.   Meehan[74] gives an account of
a horse that was exhibited in London in the early 90's of the last century.   Pawing with his hoof, this horse apparently was able to count
and answer questions in arithmetic, and among other accomplishments
he was supposed also to be able to understand something of language.
In reality, however, he merely responded to cues which were disclosed
to the reporter by the trainer.   In pawing, the horse was guided by
movements of the trainer, and in nodding or shaking the head he repu-
tedly got his cue from the inflections of the man's voice.   Is it not probable that in this latter case it was the movements which accompanied
speech that were alone effective in inducing the nod or the shake of the
head, so that the exhibiter was deceiving not merely the public, but also
himself?   Perhaps we may also doubt the exposition made by the well-
known hippologist, Colonel Spohr.[75]   He tells us that it is easy to train
horses to raise the left foot or the right foot in response to the commands " Left—foot ! " or " Right—foot ! " and that it will be the fore
foot when one is standing in front of the horse, and the hind foot if one
stands near the rear.   It cannot be so very difficult, he thinks, even to
get the horse to understand the commands " Left (or right)—fore foot ! "
and " Left (or right)—hind foot ! "—and all without any other aids
but the spoken words.   Should this really be possible without even
the slightest kind of designating movement ?——The following case,
again, I believe is undoubtedly based upon a misinterpretation.   Redding[76] relates concerning his nineteen-year old horse that he himself had
owned for thirteen years, and had always kept in single harness,——
that this horse not only understood the meaning of a long list of words,
such as : bureau, post-office, school, churchyard, apple, grass, etc.,
but he also knew a number of persons by name, as well as their
places of residence.   If he were told in advance to halt at a certain resi-

It is easy to explain the musical accomplishments. The tones which were played for the horse, were known to Mr. von Osten, since he himself played the harmonica, or when someone else played it, he, Mr. von Osten, could see the stoppers. He then thought of the number

dence, he would do it without any further aid from the driver. For this reason the happy owner felt certain that the animal possessed a high order of intelligence and "that this horse does reason." What sources of error were here operative, whether signs were given by means of reins, or head or arm movements, could be determined only by a careful examination of the case.

And finally we would exercise some reserve in entertaining the suggestions for the acoustic education of horses which have come from various sources. Colonel Spohr [77] whom we have just been mentioning, thinks that it would not be a difficult matter to get a horse to respond with a walk to one smack of the lips, with a trot to two smacks, and with a galop to three, and then he could be made to slacken his pace once more into a trot in response to one long-drawn "Pst!" and to stop in response to two. Others have gone even further. Decroix,[78] at one time leader in veterinary affairs in France, conceived the idea of working out a universal language as regards the commands that are given to horses, in the humane purpose of sparing them the whip. He called it "Volapük hippique." For the commands "go," "right," "left," and "halt," he suggests these : "Hi!" "Ha!" "Hé!" and "Ho!" respectively. From these it was possible to make eight combinations, such as "Hi! Hi!" for "Trot!" "Hé! Hé!" for "Left about" (while the single "Hé" was to mean "Forward, to the left!") "Ho! Ho!" for "Back!" etc. Decroix thought that the whole system could be inculcated in a very few lessons. He even had a medal struck which was to be awarded to the driver or rider who should first exhibit a horse, thus instructed, to the Société Nationale d'Acclimatation de France (of which Decroix was president). Eight years have elapsed since then, but we have heard of no one who has earned the medal mentioned. In the future greater care will probably be exercised in the putting forth of such suggestions, and two sources of error may be guarded against, viz.: involuntary movements on the part of the rider or driver, and imitation of the horses amongst themselves. (One horse, guarded by an experienced rider, may serve as copy for ten others with inexperienced men in the saddle.)

which indicated the tone in question, and Hans would tap it. Thus arose the tale of the horse's absolute tonal memory. This tale gained much support at the time, from an experience which has been recounted to me by the well-known composer, Professor Max Schillings. It shows more clearly than any other report how very confused were the threads that had been spun in the whole matter. In order to test the horse's musical ability Prof. Schillings played, let us say, three tones upon the accustomed instrument. Complying with Mr. von Osten's wish, Prof. Schillings always indicated which three he was about to play. The horse always tapped them correctly. In order to make a decisive test, Prof. Schillings then played, without anyone's knowledge, a note that was in reality a third below the one he had indicated to Mr. von Osten. Curiously enough, Hans tapped, as a matter of fact, the number indicating the note that was actually struck, and it was only in the third repetition and after many exhortations on the part of the master " to have a care ", that the horse finally tapped the number indicating the note Mr. von Osten had in mind and which in truth was the wrong one. This curious experiment seemed to those to whom Professor Schillings communicated it, to yield conclusive evidence of the horse's absolute hearing. As a matter of fact, however, Prof. Schillings had unwittingly, and, contrary to any intention on his part, inspired the horse. Standing, as he did, just behind the right shoulder of the horse, he was able to interrupt Hans (who had begun to tap in response to a move on the part of Mr. von Osten,) by means of an involuntary movement which did the work of a closing signal. At the same time Mr. von Osten, likewise standing to the right of the horse and expecting more taps, remained perfectly quiet. (This is as it was in the tests, mentioned on page 71, in which, of two experimenters, one started the horse tapping, and the other stopped him.) Mr. von Osten very probably lost patience after Hans had seemingly given the wrong response twice, and thereupon came nearer to the horse and thus by monopolizing its attention—so as to exclude Prof. Schillings—he was able to get the response so ardently desired.* When, in tests such as these, two stoppers

* General Noizet [79] has left us a story of the middle of the last century, which in essential detail corresponds closely with the one just given. The scene is a French chateau and the hero is—a rapping table, highly prized on account of the intelligent answers it could give. Seated about it were a number of ladies and at the other end of the room sat a French savant, a member of the Academy. The ladies requested him to put a simple mathematical question to the table, and complying with their request, he asked for the cube root of 4. None of the ladies who sat about the table knew the solution ; the table unhesitatingly gave 6 raps. This answer was refused as incorrect. The table was asked to try again, and again it wrapped 6. For this it was bitterly reproached. Hereupon the questioner, who during the whole time had remained in his place at the other end of the room, came forward with the confession that the table was innocent, that he had made a mistake. He had asked for the cube root of 4, but had really meant to ask for the cube of that number, viz., 64, and the table had as a matter of fact given the first numeral of that number.

One is immediately struck by the analogy between this case and that of Professor Schillings. In both cases those immediately concerned (the women in the one, Mr. von Osten in the other) believe that a wrong answer is being given repeatedly. The cause of the error lies in a person who seemingly is not concerned with the response. (The Frenchman asked the question, but did not sit at the table. Professor Schillings sounded the notes, but it was Mr. von Osten who got the horse to tap.) In both instances the questioner asks one thing, but had something else in mind. (With the Frenchman it was a slip of the tongue ; Mr. Schillings did it purposely.) And finally, in both cases the response corresponds not to the question that has been asked, but to that which has been thought, so that, though seemingly wrong, the responses of both were opened and thus two notes sounded, Mr. von Osten would count the number of stoppers intervening between the two, and Hans would tap the number. And so arose the tale of Hans's knowledge of musical intervals. Whenever the two notes were sung or whistled, in which case there would be no stoppers that could be counted, then Mr. von Osten, who was quite destitute of musical knowledge, was at a loss, and also Hans. If, however, the intervening notes were sung, then everything went smoothly once more. Major and minor chords were regularly characterized as " beautiful ", all others as " bad ", (but even here errors occurred). A musician had taught Mr. von Osten these distinctions. The old man also knew the melodies that were played on the hand-organ. Each one had a number assigned to it, and Hans was required to tap the number of the melody in token of recognition.—Hans was as ignorant of musical time, as he was of melody ,and all attempts to get him to march in regular step were utterly futile. A number of musical tests were made in the absence of Mr. von Osten. In these Mr. Hahn undertook the questioner's rôle, and

table and horse were really correct. By way of explanation, Noizet believes that he has a case of true thought-transference or "telepathy" (page 108). The questioner watched with utmost attentiveness the rapping of the table, and the women in turn regarded the man. And thus, Noizet believes, the man's thought was transferred to the minds of the others without the mediation of eye or ear, etc., and hence unvitiated by the words that had been spoken. I myself prefer another explanation. At that moment in which the rapping arrived at the expected number, the Frenchman executed a movement characteristic of release of tension and to this the women of the circle reacted. It was not necessary that they should be able to account for this afterward, (just as sometimes occurs in the case of thought-readers [80]). It is very probable, too, that they were not of a very reflective turn of mind anyway. We are warranted, I think, in regarding the two cases as identical in kind.

since he had had musical training, he was aware of what the numbers should be, even when he could not see the stoppers of the harmonica, and, therefore, we readily understand why it was that the horse responded so wonderfully in his case.

The so-called musical ability of horses appears, from all that is known, to be confined within very narrow bounds. Only one fact is universally accepted, viz., horses of the military are believed to possess a knowledge of the significance of trumpet signals, and are often said to interpret them more readily than the recruits.[81] Since no experiments had been made along these lines, I undertook to make a brief test of the cavalry horses mentioned on page 188. As in the preceding tests, the three animals were arranged behind one another with the customary distance of two horses' lengths between, and each was ridden by his accustomed rider. They were held by the reins, but received no aid of any kind, either to start them or to restrain them. A bugle then sounded the various signals at the other end of the barrack's courtyard. We had been previously assured that the horses would certainly react without fail. But, as a matter of fact, the result was quite the contrary. Two of the horses did not move at all, and the third, a thirteen-year old gelding, was startled nearly every time and would tear off in a gallop— even though a trot had been sounded. I would not, however, venture to draw any conclusions from results such as these. Many more tests would have to be made, and some of them upon the whole squadron, before a judgment could be given.*

* Frofessor Flügel,[82] basing his statements on an article appearing in " Schorer's Familienblatt " (Berlin, 1890, No. 8, p. 128), gives an account of similar experiments which were supposed to have been conducted by

I shall now turn to peculiarities of character, highly humanized, which have been attributed to Hans. His "sympathies" and "antipathies", so-called, were nothing but erroneous appellations for the success or failure on the part of the respective individuals to elicit responses. He who could procure answers frequently, apparently stood high in the horse's favor. That Hans shook his head violently when asked by Mr. von Osten: "Do you like Mr. Stumpf?", and answered in the affirmative the further question: "Do you like Mr. Busch?", was nothing but a confession—unwilling, to be sure—on the part of the master himself. In the first case the master thought "no", in the second instance, "yes", and the

the Zoological Society for Westphalia and Lippe, and presumably showed that "the horses of the military do not understand the bugle calls." No matter how well trained a horse may have been, it would not respond to a signal. This report, however, is due to a mistake. Such experiments have never been made by the society mentioned, so I am told by its director, Dr. Reeker. Nor do I know of any one else who has made experiments of this kind. However, Professor Landois,[83] the eminent zoologist, now deceased (founder of the scientific society mentioned), tested four circus-horses for their musical ability and specifically for their sense of musical time. He arrives at the conclusion that horses "have no feeling for time, whatsoever." With but few exceptions,[84,85] all experts to-day are of the same opinion. Horse-trainers, especially, are universally agreed on this point. It is easy to see in any circus performance that it is not the horses that accommodate themselves to the music, but that the music accommodates itself to them, and that the trained horses[86] are induced to do their artistic stepping only by the aids given by their riders. Furthermore, all these horses are trained without the use of music.————It would therefore appear that the time had arrived when the tales of the dancing horses of the Sybarites ought no longer to gain credence. Two Greek writers, Athenaeus[87] and Ælian,[88] tell us that the inhabitants of Sybaris, far-famed for their luxurious habits, had trained their horses to dance to the music of flutes during their banquets. Building upon this, the men of Crotona, in one of their campaigns against the Sybarites, ordered the flute-players to

two thoughts were accompanied by the corresponding
head movements, to which Hans responded mechanically.
Hans appeared to be well-disposed toward me, but evidently because I always rewarded him liberally when he
answered correctly, and I did not scold him when his
responses were wrong, as did Mr. von Osten and Mr.
Schillings, who instead of seeking the cause within themselves, were always ready to rebuke Hans for his con-
trariety and fickleness. The horse did not show, in so
far as can be judged at all, any real affection for his
master. On the other hand it would be unwarranted to
say that, in spite of all rewards, he developed a grudge
against all those who bothered him with instruction and
examination. Shortly after the close of our experimenta-

play the tunes familiar to the Sybarite horses. Immediately the well-
trained steeds began to dance, thus throwing the whole Sybarite army
into confusion, and the men of Crotona won the day. (The same story
is told in more detail concerning the horses of the inhabitants of Cardia.
Both accounts, somewhat mixed, are to be found in Julius Africanus,[89]
a writer of the third century of the Christian era.)—In recent years a
French veterinary surgeon, Guénon,[90] experimented on the effect of
music upon the horses of the military. He entered their stalls, playing
upon a flute, and noted their behavior. Four-fifths of the animals, he
says, were deeply moved, yes, delighted, even, ("charmés." One inter-
preter [91] calls it a case of hypnosis !). This emotional excitement was
expressed—somewhat unaesthetically —by the dropping of excrementa.
Guénon characterizes the feeling-state of these animals as being a mixture of pleasure and astonishment, of satisfaction and excitement
("mélange de plaisir et d'étonnement, de satisfaction et de trouble.")
He also asserts that the horse's musical taste is similar to our own. But
I can find nothing in his whole exposition which might prove this. Indeed there is nothing that could be interpreted as anything other than
a purely sensuous effect upon the horses. I may go a step farther and
say that thus far the sense of music, i. e., understanding of melody,
harmony and rhythm, has not been shown to exist in any animal. Some
animals may, however, be susceptible to the sensuous pleasantness of
the tones themselves.

tion it happened that Hans severely injured his groom by a blow in the face. Yet this man had always been very gentle with the horse and had been forbidden by Mr. von Osten to make Hans solve any problems for him. Experts assure me that we have here to deal, not with a case of " moral insanity ", but with a very common experience,—although this view will probably be cavilled at by enthusiastic lovers of horses. The work of so excellent an expert as Fillis,[92] for instance, bears us out in this respect.

The horse's supposed fickleness was nothing but a token of the fact that even those who were accustomed to working with him, did not have him completely in hand. (They simply did not understand how to obtain correct responses from the horse.) It often happened that in the evening, when it had become so dark that the movements of Mr. von Osten could no longer be seen, Hans had to suffer bitter reproaches because he made so many errors. That, in truth, he never was stubborn and that the cause of failure really lay in the questioner, is shown by the fact that the mood, for which he was reproved, would disappear the moment the questioner voluntarily controlled the signals. We may add that there was no basis for the assumption that " he had an uncommon, finely constituted nervous system " or was possessed of a " high degree of nervousness ". Both these phrases were often mentioned by way of explanation. Hans was restive, as horses usually are. And besides, he lived a life so secluded (he was never allowed to leave the courtyard) that as a result he was easily disturbed by strange sights and sounds. There was not the slightest trace of the clinical symptoms of neurasthenia—on the contrary he gave the impression of perfect health,—which was curious enough when we remember his rather unnatural mode of life.

Hans's stubbornness was a myth. He was suspected of it whenever the same error occurred a number of times in succession, i. e., when the questioner did not properly regulate his attention (page 146) or when he was being controlled by "perseverative tendency", mentioned on page 149. Mr. Schillings, who has provided me with material here as elsewhere, relates the following episode which occurred on one such occasion. To one and the same question put alternately by Mr. von Osten and Mr. Schillings, Hans responded correctly, with two taps, to the former, and just as persistently incorrectly, with three taps, to the latter. After Mr. Schillings had suffered this to occur three times he accosted the horse peremptorily: " And now are you going to answer correctly?". Hereupon Hans promptly shook his head, to the great merriment of all those present. (Mr. Schillings had, with no accounted reason, expected a " no ".) Hans was called willful whenever the same question was successively answered by different responses, as frequently happened with the increasing tension that characterized the high numbers (page 145). He was also regarded as stubborn when no reply at all was forthcoming, as in the tests with the blinders.

Hans's supposed distrust of the questioner, when the latter did not know the answer to the problem, is nothing but a poor attempt to account for the failure of those tests. Hans's distrust of the correctness of his own responses was supposed to be evident from his tendency to begin to tap once more if, after the completion of a task, the questioner did not immediately give expression to some form of approval or disapproval—just as a school-boy begins to doubt his answer if the teacher remains silent for a short time. In terms of the results of our experimentation this would mean that whenever the questioner did not resume the erect posture, after Hans had given the final tap with the left foot, then the horse would immediately begin once more to tap with the other foot (page 61).

As the evil characteristics, so, too, the good. Thus, his precipitancy, which was supposedly evidenced by his beginning to tap before the questioner had enunciated the question, was nothing but a reflection of the questioner's own precipitancy in bending forward (page 57). Never did Hans evince the slightest trace of spontaneity. He never spelled, of his own accord, anything like " Hans is hungry," for instance. He was rather like a machine that must be started and kept going by a certain amount of fuel (in the form of bread and carrots). The desire for food did not have to be operative in every case. The tapping might ensue mechanically as a matter of habit—for horses are to a large extent creatures of habit. This lack of spontaneity could hardly be reconciled with the horse's reputation for cleverness. It would not be necessary to touch upon the signs that were supposed to betoken genius: the intelligent eye, the high forehead, the carriage of the head, which clearly showed that " a real thought process was going on inside ",—all these, we said, would not need mentioning, if they had not been taken seriously by sober-minded folk. If there is a report that Hans turned appreciatively toward visitors who made some remark in praise of his accomplishments,—it is evidence only of the observer's imaginativeness.

Turning from a consideration of the horse to that of

the persons experimenting with him,* the first and most important question that arises is this: How was it possible that so many persons (there were about forty) were

* I cannot enter upon a discussion of the latest psychological problems, here involved, partly because that would take us beyond the purpose of this monograph, and partly because they are still moot questions and hence not suited to popular treatment. Briefly though, they are these : What is the nature of the relationship between cognitive and affective states on the one hand and involuntary, (so-called expressive) movements on the other? Is this connection an external thing, as it were, an association arising as a habit formation, or does every idea partake essentially of a motor character? Do purely cognitive states give rise to such movements, or does the movement impulse depend more particularly upon the affective consciousness accompanying the cognitive states? And in how far do given kinds of expressive movements depend upon certain ideational types (c.f. page 95)? Thus, what is the influence of the visual image upon the gestures for " up," " down," etc. ? And then, are these involuntary movements, when not noted, truly unconscious, or merely not attended to,—— in other words, are they beyond the pale of consciousness or merely " at the fringe ? " The various writers speak almost without exception of unconscious movements in the strict sense of the term. My own introspections, however, have led me to doubt whether they are quite unconscious. Since I have attained some practice I am able to describe in detail (under conditions of objective control) my involuntary movements, no matter how slight, even down to mere muscular tensions. None of my subjects, however, has as yet succeeded in this. It is no very easy matter to be on the lookout for some unknown movements which might eventually occur, while attempting to concentrate attention to the utmost upon a certain definite ideational content, for this very dividing of attention effects a decrease in the force of the movement, and thus makes it all the more difficult to discover. From my own experience, however, I am inclined to believe that these movements are not unconscious, but merely unattended to, in other words, we have a narrowing down of the apperceived content within certain limits, but not a narrowing down of consciousness, (much less a " splitting " of consciousness or of personality as the thing unfortunately has sometimes been called). In order, however, not to be guilty of premature judgment, I have avoided the terms " unconscious " and " unattended to," and chose expressions which leave these finer distinctions untouched.

able to receive responses from the horse, and many of them on the very first occasion? The answer is not hard to find. All of these persons came to the horse in very much the same frame of mind—which found a similar expression in all, in both posture and movements. And it was these motor expressions of the questioner (aside from the signs for " yes " and " no ", which I believe I have adequately explained on page 98), that the horse needed as stimuli for his activity.

The next question that arises is: why did only a few persons receive responses regularly from Hans, whereas the greater number were favored only occasionally? What was the selective principle involved? The answer is, that the successful person had to belong to a certain type, which embodied the following essential characteristics.

1. A certain measure of ability and tact in dealing with the horse. As in the case of dealing with wild animals, such as the lion, etc., Hans must not be made uneasy by timidity in the questioner, but must be approached with an air of quiet authority.

2. The power of intense concentration, whether in expectation of a certain sensory impression (the final tap), or in fixing attention upon some idea-content (" yes ", " no ", etc.). It is only when expectancy and volition are very forceful, that a sufficient release of tension can ensue. This release of tension is accompanied by a change in innervation and results in a perceptible movement. And it was only when the thought of " yes ", or " up ", etc., was very vivid, that the nervous energy would spread to the motor areas and thence to the efferent fibers, and thus result in the head-movement of the questioner.

From infancy we are trained to keep all of our voluntary muscles under a certain measure of control. During the state of concentration just described, this control is relaxed, and our whole musculature becomes the instrument for the play of non-voluntary impulses. The stronger the customary control, the stronger must the stimuli be which can overcome it. The steady unremitting fixation, which resulted in the horse's selection of the cloths, also involves a high degree of concentration.

3. Facility of motor discharge. Great concentration was necessary of course, but not sufficient. Persons in whom the flow of nervous energy tended to drain off over the nerves leading to the glands and the vascular system might betray great tension, not so much by movements as by a flow of perspiration (we have many excellent examples of this given by Manouvrier) [93] or by a violent beating of the heart, blushing and the like,—in short, by secretory and vasomotor effects. Or it is not inconceivable that long dealing with very abstract thoughts might have weakened the tendency of overflow to other parts of the brain, and that therefore the entire discharge is used up in those portions of the brain which are the basis of the intellectual processes. But if expressive movements occur, the motor pathways must be particularly unresisting in order to take up the overflow of psychophysic energy. This is the necessary condition for obtaining the tapping and the head movements on the part of the horse, although for the tapping there is still one other circumstance necessary: viz.,

4. The power to distribute tension economically—i. e., the ability to sustain it long enough, and to release it at the right moment (after the manner of the curves de-

scribed on page 93), and to control properly the unavoidable variations which will occur.*

* The mental state just described is probably essentially the same as that of the spiritualistic " mediums " when they are occupied with table-rapping and table-moving. In both·cases concentration is very intense,—— in other words, the field of attention is limited. We saw that this state not only favors the tendency toward involuntary movement, but on account of the absorption of the individual's attention by a certain limited content, the person will be unaware of the voluntary movements as they occur. And we are not necessarily here dealing with neurasthenic, hysteric, or other diseased nervous conditions. In the case of table-rapping there are movements of the hands, in our case there are those of the head. Our head, balanced as it is upon the cervical vertebral column, is continually in a state of unstable equilibrium and therefore peculiarly susceptible to movement-impulses of every kind. But I could induce not only movements of the head, but also of the arms and legs, and this by having the subject assume a posture which enabled him to hold arms or legs in as unstable a position as possible. He might stretch out his legs horizontally before him, or he could raise them vertically upward as in the hand-stand in gymnastic work. An extract from a treatise by Count A. de Gasparin,[94] which appeared about the middle of the last century, may serve to show how close the correspondence between the two processes, that of getting the table to rap and that of causing Hans to respond, really is. The report of this writer, based upon the detailed record of his tests in table-moving and table-rapping, closely parallels in many minute detail the observations which were made in the course of our experimentation with Hans. The case is all the more remarkable when we bear in mind that this writer did not seek the cause of the phenomena, as we did, in involuntary movements, but thrusting aside this explanation, he posited the cause in the agency of some mysterious fluid. It may not be amiss to say that this as well as most other references were consulted after the present experiments and introspections had been completed. Of the page references preceding the following citations, the first always refers to the page in the French original, and the other, enclosed in brackets, to the parallel passage in the present monograph.

P. 49 [31]. Some questioners are especially suitable (" experimentateurs hors ligne "), but in their absence, other persons may also operate successfully (" le succès, quoique moins brillant alors, n'est pas impossible.")

The experience of a number of practical men, who have had much to do with horses and yet achieved but

P. 25 [229]. But even the most suitable questioners do not always succeed equally well ("les plus sûrs d'eux-mêmes ne réussissaient pas également tous les jours.")

P. 42 [151]. When the questioner is in any way indisposed, the measure of success is also less.

P. 91 & 87 [150]. The Questioner must first get into the sweep of things ("en train"), and once he has done so, all interruption whatsoever must be avoided.

P. 91 [93]. Unless there is sufficient tension on the part of the questioner, the test will fail. ("La volonté est-elle absente, rien ne bouge.")

P. 210 [93]. When there is too low a degree of tension, then too great a number will be tapped ("si votre volonté ne les [les tables] arrête pas au moment où se termine le chiffre pensé, elles continueront indéfiniment.")

P. 31 [93]. But too great concentration of attention will also produce failure ("s'il n'arrivait.... de désirer trop fortement le succès et de m'impatienter en cas de retard, je n'avais plus aucune action sur la table.")

P. 36 [151]. If the proper mood ("entrain habituel") is wanting and the tests are unsuccessful, it is best not to attempt some new and difficult experiment, but to turn to some that are simpler and more entertaining ("La table obéissait mal; les coups étaient frappés mollement et comme à regret. .... Alors nous avons pris un parti dont nous nous sommes bien trouvés; nous avons persévéré, et persévéré gaiement;.... nous avons écarté la pensée des tentatives nouvelles, et insisté sur les opérations aisées et amusantes. Après un certain temps les dispositions étaient changées, la table bondissait et attendait à peine nos commandements.")

P. 199 [41, 90]. It is not necessary to enunciate the questions aloud ("On est convenu que celui qui commanderait ne prononcerait pas à haute voix le nombre de coups, mais se contenterait de les penser, après les avoir communiqués à l'oreille de son voisin. Eh bien! la table a obéi. Il n'y a jamais eu la moindre erreur.")

P. 199 [64 ff.]. The large numbers are tapped more rapidly than the small ones ("la table a indiqué notre âge tel qu'il était dans notre esprit, se hâtant même de la manière la plus comique lorsque le nombre des coups à frapper était un peu considérable.")

P. 210 [35 ff.]. Tests in which "procedure was without knowledge" very modest success with Hans, goes to show that it is not always the lack of sufficient authoritativeness, mentioned under heading 1 that is the sole cause of failure, as has been claimed so often. That the horse was, to a certain degree, influenced by this element of authority is shown, however, by the following incident. A certain gentleman, when alone in the courtyard with Hans, received responses only so long as I (concealed in the barn) kept the barn-door open just a little, so that my presence could be known to the horse. As soon as I closed the door, Hans refused to respond to the gentleman. Those who possessed sufficient power of concentration and the requisite motor tendency—the two characteristics mentioned under 1 and 2 above,—were able to obtain responses from the horse without any previous practice. Practice merely effected a more economic distribution of attention, so that the larger numbers especially were more successful as a result (pages 68 and 89). Those who were lacking in either of the characteristics mentioned under 2 and 3 would not be aided even by the greatest amount of practice, as is shown by the case men-

failed completely (" Les tables ne révèlent pas ce qui n'est pas dans la pensée et dans la volonté de l'expérimentateur; quand on veut les charger d'autre chose que d'obéir comme des membres, on arrive à des erreurs continuelles.")

P. 28, 29, 217 [72]. When of two experimenters each tries to get the horse to tap a different number, then that one who is the better able to compel the animal's attention, will be the successful one. (" L'un veut faire prévaloire un chiffre pensé plus considérable, l'autre un chiffre pensé moins considérable .... Eh bien: l'opérateur le plus puissant l'emporte." "Ainsi A est chargé secrètement de faire frapper 25 coups, B est chargé secrètement de l'arrêter à 18; A l'emporte, et les 25 coups s'achèvent.... On fait maintenant l'inverse : B est chargé secrètement de faire frapper 13 coups; A est chargé secrètement de l'arrêter à 7; A l'emporte encore et le chiffre 7 ne peut être dépassé.")

tioned in Supplement III (page 255).—That many individuals were at first successful but were later unable to get any successful responses, is to be accounted for by the fact that the power of concentration, at first present, later rapidly disappeared. This temporary increase in the power of doing mental work was first investigated experimentally by Rivers and Kraepelin,[95] and was called by them " Antrieb " and aptly likened to the first pull of a team of horses in starting off. This, too, explains an experience which befell a number of the horse's visitors, who later described it to me. Wishing to utilize a momentary absence of Mr. von Osten, they excitedly put a hasty question to Hans, and with amazing regularity received correct responses.—Besides Mr. von Osten, Mr. Schillings and myself, not many were always able to induce Hans to bring the colored cloths or to execute the head movements. It was easy, on the other hand, to get him to nod. Therefore there was some truth in Mr. von Ostens' assertion, that Hans would be unable to answer a difficult question if he had not previously indicated by means of a nod that he had grasped its import. Those who were not concentrating sufficiently, would not look into Hans's face, when he was expected to nod, and would not bend over, when Hans ought to begin tapping—such persons could not, therefore, since they did not induce Hans to nod, elicit the tapping. I, myself saw the " no " successfully elicited only in the case of Mr. von Osten, Mr. Schillings and Mr. Hahn; the " right " and " left " only in the case of the former two. It must remain uncertain whether this failure on the part of otherwise suitable persons to elicit the responses for " right " and " left " was due to their accompanying these ideas by movements of the eyes instead of by movements of the head, (page 106). For unfortunately it was not possible to make special tests to discover whether Hans reacted to isolated eye movements. There is, however, more than one reason why I would doubt this. Taken all in all, there were but few persons who were entirely representative of the type described (c. f. page 31)—they were those who are commonly characterized as being of a lively temperament and strongly impulsive. Thus Hans acquired a reputation for "Einkennigkeit", that is, he would accustom himself only to certain persons. Such a reputation was hard to reconcile with his much praised intelligence.

In closing, just a word on the influence of the public that was present. As was shown on page 69, the public in general did not influence the horse in his reactions. The effect upon the questioner, however, was unmistakable, and worked in a twofold manner. On the one hand the questioner's zeal was increased and with it the tension of concentration. On the other hand, it introduced an element of diversion, and attention was divided between the horse and the spectators, and thus concentration suffered. If the disturbing effect was slight, as in the case of Mr. von Osten, then the favorable influence exercised by the presence of the public outweighed the unfavorable. Mr. von Osten was, for that reason, often particularly successful when working in the presence of a large body of spectators. This was noted by many and was ascribed to the ambition of the horse. When, however, a person was easily diverted, as was Mr. Schillings, then the presence of the public had a less fortunate effect.

This, then, completes my explanation of the facts gleaned from observation and experimentation. It accomplishes all, I hope, that may be expected of an explanation. All the known achievements of the horse, all the successes and failures of the questioner, have been reduced to a single principle; no secondary hypothesis has been invoked, and but slight place has been given to the element of chance. Nevertheless, it may not be out of place to forestall two objections which might possibly be raised. First, some may assert that it was through our experimentation that the horse became mechanized and incapacitated as regards conceptual thinking; that formerly he really could solve arithmetical problems, and only later developed the very bad habit of depending upon the signs which I gave him. This objection is to be refuted in that I did not originate these signs, but first noted them in Mr. von Osten, himself, and in that Hans still works as faithfully as ever for Mr. von Osten. I have learned from many trustworthy witnesses that the horse still continues to give brilliant exhibitions of his " ability ". If, on the other hand, anyone should assert that it was only with us that Hans reacted to movements, but that with his master he really thought and still thinks, then I must ask for proof. This latter argument is by no means very original. When Faraday in 1853 proved experimentally that " table-rapping " is the result of involuntary movements on the part of the participants standing about the table, the spiritualists asserted that his experiments had nothing in common with their own proceedings, because his subjects (who by the way, had been up to that time firm believers in table-rapping) probably did move the table, they said, while they (the spiritualists) do no such thing.[96]

CHAPTER VI

GENESIS OF THE REACTION OF THE HORSE

In the preceding discussion we have regarded the achievements of the horse as well as Mr. von Osten's explanation of them, as matters of fact. Let us now consider the question: How did the horse come by these achievements, and how did its master arrive at his curious theory in explanation of them? Did he indeed seek to instill in the horse's mind the rudiments of human culture through long years of painstaking instruction in accordance with the method described in Supplement I (page 245)? If that is the case, then, of course his hoped-for success was only seeming, not real. Or did he, as so many critics aver, systematically train the horse to respond automatically to certain cues, and propound his theory merely for the purpose of misleading the public? There might possibly be another alternative, viz.: was there a mixture of instruction and of training to respond to cues?

The production of the horse's achievements would not require a great deal of explanation, if it were a case of mere training for the purpose of establishing certain responses to certain cues. It might be desirable, however, before deciding in favor of one of these possibilities, to indicate briefly the process of development, as it might occur, if the point of view is taken that *bona fide* instruction was given.

This development would probably be as follows:—Mr. von Osten, as the result of theoretical speculation or of a misinterpretation of the facts of experience, having arrived at the conclusion that the horse possessed extraordinary capacity, finally undertook to instruct a certain horse for a period covering three years. This one having died, he, nothing daunted, undertook the education of another one. What it was that influenced this old teacher of mathematics to deprive humankind of the benefit of his extraordinary pedagogical ability and love of teaching, we do not know. It may be that he had had bitter experience in that line, or again, mayhap the newness and tremendousness of this other task stimulated him. His first problem must have been to arouse the interest of the animal in this process of education. It was hardly to be believed that Hans would eagerly coöperate in a process which promised to yield him no immediate benefit. The teacher sought to overcome this lack of immediate interest by the means of rewards. To Hans the sweet carrot was as toothsome a bite as candy is to the child. And since the horse was furthermore kept on low rations on account of the relatively low amount of physical exercise he took, the anticipation of the carrots was doubly enticing.

The first thing that Mr. von Osten sought to teach the horse, according to his own statement, was the significance of the names of colors and of the spatial directions such as "up", "down", etc. In the case of children there is a simple test by means of which we may discover if they have put any content into these words. The test is: Do they, themselves, use them correctly? Do they call the blue, blue, and the red, red? Since the horse could not speak, his instructor had to give him some means by which he could make himself understood. He taught Hans to approach the colors and select the cloth of the color wanted. He also taught him to make those movements of the head or body which correspond with the expressions: " up ", " down ", etc.

First of all, Hans had to be taught to bring the cloths. Then began the pointing out of the different colors, accompanied each time by their proper names. It is very probable that at first Hans had to be led each time to each separate colored cloth and taught to raise it or to touch it with his nose. Later, Mr. von Osten, after having pronounced the name of the color, remained at his place, with his head and body directed to the cloth in question and gazing intently at it, in order to see whether or not the horse was pointing out the right one. Naturally Hans would, at first, fail a hundred times where he would succeed but once, but since the horse would receive the anticipated reward in case of success, he gradually became conscious that this reward was attached to executions which had some special mark. This special mark would be expressed in human speech by the statement that the horse would go in the direction indicated by the position of the instructor's body. For Hans, of course, this would not take the form of an abstract statement, but simply of a definite way of seeing and of going and a correlation of the two in a certain definite manner,—the whole being a process, the elements of which remained unanalyzed and unaccounted for by Hans. Owing to the position of the eye, it was possible for him to keep his master within his field of vision, while he was approaching the cloths. And only when he had correlated his approach in a certain definite manner with his visual perception of the master, i. e., only when he had felt his way, as it were, along the latter's line of vision, did he receive his reward. A sufficient number of repetitions was all that was necessary to establish an association in the psychological sense of the term. In the same manner, dogs will learn, as was indicated on page 177, to bring an object upon which the master has fixed his gaze, it mattering little whether or not the name of the object be enunciated. There is only this difference, that, in the case of the dog it is not possible to keep the image of the master within the field of vision; but neither is it necessary, for he has recognized the object before he has started for it. We must remember, however, that it does not simplify an attempt at explanation to assume that Mr. von Osten consciously trained the animal to respond to certain bodily positions of the questioner. For, even in this case, it would be necessary to explain how it was possible for him to train the horse to heed the cues.—In the course of time, the instructor may have noticed that whenever he moved during the course of a test the horse invariably failed. But he may have regarded this merely as an incidental distraction and afterward was careful to remain quiet. As soon as he increased the number of cloths upon the floor, it was no longer possible for him to give the horse such accurate directive signs, and the number of errors consequently increased. Ascribing them to the inattentiveness of his pupil, he sought to encourage him by such calls as " look out ", " look there ", " see there ", believing that, thus, he was directing the horse's attention to the desired color. Without understanding the meaning of the calls, Hans learned, however, to keep moving just as long as the calling continued, for if he did this he was regularly rewarded. An association was established between the call and the impulse to move on. And with these two associations established, Hans gave the impression of having grasped the meaning of the color terms.

The origin of the proper movements in response to the terms " up " and " down " may be explained by the fact that the movements themselves were practised in a purely external fashion. Thus, whenever the word " left " was pronounced, the horse's head was pulled to the left by means of the bridle or the reward was held off to that side. Later, Mr. von Osten, who looked expectpectantly at the horse's head, whenever he pronounced the word would unconsciously move his own head in the direction in which he desired the horse to turn. This is quite in accord with the words of Darwin to the effect that whenever we wish an object to move in a certain direction it is well-nigh impossible for us to inhibit an unconscious, involuntary movement in that direction. Proof for this may be found on all sides, in daily experience.[97] Imagine, for instance, the strain sensations of the bowler or billiard player as he follows the moving ball. It is impossible to decide whether Mr. von Osten, consciously continued to image the head movements which he expected the horse to make or whether these anticipatory images later remained below the threshold as was always the case with Mr. Schillings and myself (see page 100). But this question is of little significance, for even assuming that he always thought of the movement he expected on the part of the horse, this by no means implies that he was conscious of the movements on his part, which were associated with the thought process.

Everything up to this point might be explained as the working of simple memory association, but when we come to problems in counting and arithmetical calculation, we are in the field of conceptual thought. Here, again, it was necessary for Mr. von Osten to invent a suitable means of expression for the horse, and once more this had to be borrowed from the treasury of gesture-language. Tapping with the hoof was naturally hit upon as one of the normal, expressive movements of the horse. This has long been used by trainers, in preparing horses for show purposes. The method used in training the horse to make this response is of no import, whether it was by touching his foot with the hand, or tapping his leg, or by any other means.

It is possible that many will declare, as being nonsensical, any attempt to introduce number-concepts * into an animal's mind, because the necessary motor basis is lacking. We will not, just at this point, stop to discuss whether or not it was not possible to develop number-concepts from purely auditory or visual representations. It is evident, however, that Mr. von Osten believed that a motor basis of some sort was essential. In the case of man this basis is found in the enunciation of the number names (or in the manipulation of the fingers). Mr. von Osten seemed to think that he was justified in assuming that, even in the case of the horse, some form of inner articulation of the word-sounds was possible;—at the same time, in so doing, he did not blink at the psychological difficulty of this hypothesis. The tapping of the foot was to be regarded merely as the expression of the process of inner counting, but not as the motor basis of the process. For this latter purpose tapping would be quite inadequate, for the number complexes which arise in the summation process of counting, could not be dif-

---

* The author intends to take up the problem of counting, so-called, on the part of animals and of the principle involved, in another work soon to be forthcoming.

ferentiated by mere tapping with the foot, any more than a child could learn to count by employing only one finger. Mr. von Osten evidently imagined the process was somewhat like this: Whenever Hans was about to count 5, he would enunciate inwardly the numbers from 1 to 5, and would accompany each word with a tap of the foot. Since, furthermore, wooden pins and balls could be used—as in the case of children—for giving visual content in learning the significance of the number-terms, it seemed as if all the conditions necessary for the formation of number-concepts were supplied. However, the most essential thing had to be presupposed, viz.: that the horse virtually possessed the general power of forming concepts,* and that all that had been lacking was the suitable conditions for its development. Mr. von Osten held tenaciously to this conviction, and it was this conviction that was the basis for the infinite patience with which the tests had been pursued.

To come now to the learning process itself;—we may assume that, at first, whenever the horse began to tap in response to commands, he would receive a reward for this purely mechanical feat. Wooden pins were then planted on the ground and designated as: one, one two, etc., and

---

* There are some who believe they are warranted in concluding the opposite from the structure of the animal's brain alone. We may say that the brain of the horse, compared with that of the ape, or even that of the dog, represents a relatively low type of development. But owing to the rapid changes in the views, often contradictory, concerning the nature of the nervous structures and processes underlying the thought process, any conclusion based on such views would be premature. For this reason we cannot agree with the French physiologist who was dissecting the brain of a horse and, struck by its smallness of size, exclaimed: "When I saw your proud look and beautiful neck, I hesitated a moment before mounting upon your back. But now that I have seen how small is your brain, I no longer have any qualm about using you." [98]

each time someone would raise the horse's foot as many times as the count demanded (see Supplement I).   Then Mr. von Osten would take his stand at the horse's side and would command him, let us say, to tap 3.   Hans noting merely (from his master's position) that he was expected to tap, would begin.   The instructor, who had bent forward in order to watch the horse tapping,* would involuntarily straighten up again at the third tap, without being conscious of it and quite unaware that he was thus giving a signal.   The horse would be startled, and sometimes he would immediately cease tapping and sometimes not.   But it was only in the first case that he would receive a reward.   Thus, unknown to the instructor, an association became established between the sight of the upward jerk of the instructor and the act of ceasing to tap.   To be sure, the animal would receive sundry visual impressions from the wooden pins set up before him and the auditory stimulations of the spoken number names, on the basis of which, the concepts were to be formed in his mind.   But in this chaos of visual impressions (at times there were two wooden pins, then three, then four, sometimes there were the pins, at others, the balls of the counting-machine)—and in the babel of word-sounds—which evidently meant nothing but noise to him—amidst all this there was but one constant element: the final movement of the instructor's body.   The moment the horse reacted to this, he would receive the tidbit at the hands of his overjoyed master, and thus he became more and more accustomed to attend to this jerk, even after it had grad-

---

* This natural and close connection between the process of attention and the movement toward the object attended to is clearly expressed in our English and French terms, derived from the Latin " tendere ad—," to reach toward—.

ually decreased in scope. And the reason again, why this jerk tended to become less pronounced was that the tests were gradually becoming more and more successful. For, corresponding to the degree in which the horse began to react properly, the instructor's tenseness and excitement tended to decrease, and with this decrease of the emotional element in the man's consciousness, the accompanying non-voluntary, expressive movement gradually became less pronounced until it attained that extraordinary refinement which it possesses to-day. We noticed also, that whenever the horse, for any reason, had to be trained anew, Mr. von Osten's movements would, on the whole, become somewhat more gross, as for instance after the tests with the blinders. There is not a shadow of a doubt that this increase in the movement's extent was entirely unintentional, since the horse could not see his master at all on account of the blinders which had been attached to the trappings.

In the same way it is possible to explain the details. Mr. von Osten himself said that at first Hans had tapped at times with his left foot, at times with his right, just as he pleased. But later his master taught him to tap only with the right. Whenever he began with the left, Mr. von Osten would immediately interrupt him, and he was allowed to add only a final tap with his left foot. Thus, this additional tap which was sometimes made with the left foot was but the vestige of an earlier rudimentary habit. The signal for it was the stooping posture in which the master remained after the head-jerk had been made. Whenever Mr. von Osten had given Hans a small number to tap, he would bend forward only a little. But when he expected a larger number he would bend forward somewhat more, owing to the desire to observe the tapping more carefully. From the slight inclination of the master's body the horse would get the cue that he was expected to tap for a short time only, by the greater degree of inclination he would know that he was to tap for a longer period. In the second case he tapped rapidly and did not raise his foot as high from the ground—evincing a regard for the saving of energy, which may well be attributed to a horse. And thus arose the connection between the degree of inclination of the instructor's body and the horse's rate of tapping.

So, now that the ability to count and solve problems had become fixed—as the old gentleman thought—he began to instruct the horse in other branches. Since everything had been translated into terms which were to be expressed by means of tapping with the foot, and thus really put into terms of number—which was perhaps natural for an old teacher of mathematics—the same mechanism was involved in these accomplishments as in those of counting, etc. Mr. von Osten saw the animal's intelligence steadily increase, without having the slightest notion that between his words and the responsive movements of the horse, there were interpolated his own unconscious movements—and that thus instead of the much desired intellectual feats on the part of the horse, there was merely a motor reaction to a purely sensory stimulus. It has been a common custom of man to posit some extraneous cause for movements resulting from certain involuntary motions of his own, of which he is not aware, (witness the divining-rod).* And furthermore, when

* G. Franzius,[99] privy counselor of the admiralty, master of the dry-dock at Kiel, is responsible for the undeserved revival of the ancient belief, long buried by science, that the divining branch is put into motion solely as the result of the influence of hidden springs or treasures, and

these results appear to be rational, the tendency is to seek their cause in some extraneous intelligence, not his own. Just as the spiritualists ascribe the "messages" which are revealed to them through table-rapping, to certain rational spirits, so Mr. von Osten credited the intelligence of the horse with the result produced by his own involuntary signs—i. e., with the proper solution of problems.

Two other phenomena may have tended to strengthen Mr. von Osten's belief in Hans's intelligence. One was the misleading similarity with which the horse's supposed

without any agency in the person who is holding it. The untenability of this theory comes home to us most forcibly when we recall how various are the kinds of things which have been discovered by means of the branch. First there is gold and water, which are the only ones mentioned by Mr. Franzius. The water can be thus discovered only when it flows below ground, say that which is passing through the mains of a city, whereas the water of the Rhine or the Elbe would have no effect on the branch. Besides gold, every other kind of metal has been supposedly located by the branch,—as well as coal, gypsum, ochre, red-chalk sulphur and petroleum,—according to the desire of the one searching. Thus, the very same branch that just a moment ago was influenced by the least bit of underground water, may remain unaffected by the presence of a large body of water, if in the meantime I have changed my plan and decide to search for coal or for gold. But that is not all. The branch will point out a murderer or the place where a murder has been committed, it will discover the thief or his trail, as well as the things stolen or merely touched by him. It will indicate where the boundary-stone that has been moved, ought to stand. The branch further discloses the sins of the persons concerning whom it is consulted, as well as their talents and abilities, the journeys they have made and the wounds they have received. It will indicate whether or not a person has money and how much. It can announce what absent persons are doing and what apparel they are wearing, and of what color it is. It will give information on theological, medical, zoological, and botanical questions. In fine, no matter what the question, it will never fail of an answer.[100], [101]

The impossibility of explaining the phenomena in a purely physical way was recognized at a very early date. For a long time the activity

errors in computation and the poorly adjusted concentration of the questioner, were expressed. We recall the
difficulty in the case of very high numbers. This might
easily be considered as being due to the horse's ability to
work more readily with small, rather than with large
numbers, whereas, as a matter of fact, it was due solely
to the difficulty of the questioner to keep his attention
concentrated upon the number for so long a time. We
recall also the frequency of errors of one unit too few
and one unit too many. These were easily interpreted as
miscounts on the part of Hans, but in truth were the re-

of the users of the divining rod seems to have been restricted to the
search for metals. The first (or one of the first) to raise his voice
against it was the learned G. Agricola [102] (1556), and after him there
were many who all wrote more or less independently of one another.
Aside from swindle and chance, it was usually believed that sorcery of
the agency of Beelzebub was involved, and for that reason the Church
has repeatedly forbidden the use of the divining-rod. But even in the
17th century we find some who believed that it was imagination alone
that moved the person's hand, and with it the rod, [103], [104] ("fortassis
etiam phantasia manum in motum concitante"); and that points out
the essentials of the solution of the phenomenon, and we will not go
into the matter here in detail. A number of complex psychological
problems arising in connection with it are still waiting to be solved, but
this much appears certain; the staff or branch plays no other part in the
whole process than that which is served by the three levers in the tests
described in Chapter IV (pages 116 ff.),—they simply magnify the expressive movements of the diviner. And so we can understand why
the instruments serving as rod might be so varied. Hay-forks, pickets,
clock-springs and pendulums, scissors and pliers have been used. A
knife and fork or two pipes, fastened together, an open book, and even
a sausage, grasped at both ends and thus bent together somewhat,—
all have served the purpose equally well. We can understand, too, how
some adepts are able to achieve the same degree of success—for they
do succeed beyond a doubt—without any rod whatever, but simply by
placing the index fingers end to end and bending them somewhat, and
even by merely groping about with hands outstretched or folded before
them.[106]

sult of the poorly concentrated attention of the questioner. Added to this was the seeming independence and self-sufficiency of the horse. Often the number given by him was other than that desired by his master. Usually Hans was in the wrong in such cases, but sometimes, too, he was right. At any rate, this served to give the impression of independence of thought which his master so thoroughly believed he possessed, and which was the goal of his endeavors—though as a matter of fact he was farther removed than ever from that goal.

Some may ask: Does not this whole process partake of the essentials of all training, (though cumbersome and misunderstood, to be sure), and is there any need of investigating whether or not the actual development was of the sort here outlined, or whether it actually took the course common to all training?

In order to answer this question we must determine more specifically what we mean by the term "training". Usually we take it to mean the establishment in the animal, of definite habits of motor reaction in response to certain stimuli purposely selected by the trainer, and without involving any process of animal consciousness other than association. Such a conception may be applied also to man, if we assume that the higher thought processes can be eliminated. If that were the case, the above definition would not have to be changed, not even with regard to the word "animal", for we must take it in the antique sense of "zoon", a signification readopted by modern zoology. The concept may be widened, however, by omitting the differentia of "purpose", or even more, by including the habitual association of ideas or images (instead of movements) with certain sensory stimuli, But in so doing, we must bear in mind that we are going beyond the usual content which in everyday practice is put into the term " training ". Especially, when we cease to regard the presence of purpose in the trainer's mind (both in giving the stimulus as well as in the habituation of the animal to them) as essential. When this is done, the conception of training really resolves itself into the much wider conception of habit-building, and the whole discussion becomes merely a quarrel over words. In order to obviate this, let us bear in mind that in the following, the word " training " is always taken in the usual and narrower sense. The term then is still ambiguous only in so far as it has not merely its original significance of the *act* of purposely habituating (a person or an animal) to perform certain definite movements, but by transference is also used to denote the *effect,* i. e., the occurrence of the movements in question. But this does not really detract from the clearness of the concept itself.

Having cleared up the question of definition, let us return to our original problem: Does the hypothetical account of the probable development of the horse's reactions, which is given on pages 213 to 220, represent a case of training? This must be denied decidedly with regard to the tapping of numbers and the solution of arithmetical problems. For here the sensory stimuli which were purposely given, i. e., the wooden pins, the balls, and the spoken words, were intended to subserve the function of arousing not movement, but thought processes in the horse; whereas the function of the horse's movements was to give expression to these thought processes. Of the really effective stimuli—the slight movements on his part—the master was never conscious, much less were they purposely made. The same holds true for the " up " and " down ", " yes " and " no ", etc., for here also Mr. von Osten counted upon the rise of the corresponding concepts, and not merely upon a purely external, mechanical association of meaningless sounds with certain movement-responses on the part of the horse. This might also explain the genesis of Mr. von Osten's belief that Hans was able mentally to put himself in the place of the questioner, (page 19).   At any rate it is very improbable that he, Mr. von Osten himself, clearly distinguished between the concept: " up " and the sound of the word " up ".   When we come to consider the horse's selection of the colored cloths, and even more his leaping and rearing, we find that the distinction between " training " and " instruction " vanishes.   If we had to deal only with this class of achievements, we might perhaps say, without fear of going very far wrong, that the only difference between this and the ordinary form of training was that Mr. von Osten had intended to train the horse to respond to auditory signs (words), but had unintentionally trained him to respond to visual signs instead.   But it is not this type of performance that has become the bone of contention.   Just as it would be misleading to maintain that Mr. von Osten's effort was nothing other than a case of training, so it also would be unjustifiable to designate the results of his effort by that name, since the really effective stimuli were not, as has been pointed out just now, given intentionally.

As far as the horse is concerned, it is a matter of indifference whether or not really effective stimuli were given intentionally by the questioner.   The animal knows nothing of human purposes and if he were transferred to a circus, he would find nothing new in the method employed there, except the use of the whip.   We, however, define our concepts from the human and not from the horse's point of view. We may definitely say, therefore, that the method described cannot be regarded as that of training, neither in its application nor in the effect produced, though in the latter it closely simulates the effects of the training method.

Having thus differentiated between the methods of instruction and training, let us now attempt to decide on the basis of such indications as we may possess, which of the two was actually represented by the development of the horse's attainments. Surveying the facts which we have at hand, we may say that there are hosts of reasons why we cannot assume that it was a case of training. Everything that we know from our own observation and from the well-attested statements of others, with regard to the actual process of instruction, weighs against the assumption. Another evidence of this is the long period of time which Mr. von Osten required (both in the case of Hans, as well as with his predecessor), whereas the same end would have been much more speedily attained if it had been a case of training. A further argument is the fact that a large horse was selected for the purpose, whereas a small mare would have been far more suitable, (c. f., " Clever Rosa ", page 7). Again, the whip. that sorcerer's rod of all professional trainers, was here absent. And finally, many traits of character of Mr. von Osten, as well as his conduct during the whole course of events, militate against such an assumption. He generously turned the horse over to us, as he had given it over to Count zu Castell, Count Matuschka and Mr. Schillings. He eagerly besought a scientific investigation. He had made several reports to different ministries. All of these acts could only hasten the denouément. What could have been his motive? Some thought they detected an effort at pecuniary speculation, and an advertisement of June, 1902, in the " Militärwochenblatt", in which Hans was offered for sale, seemed to confirm the conjecture. Mr. von Osten says that this occurred at a time when he himself was sick and had become tired of the job. And why should he not be willing to sell even a thinking horse, since he had become convinced that any other could be instructed in the same way? Besides, I have it on good authority that after the publication of the September report he received several exorbitant offers; to mention only one of them: a local vaudeville company was ready to pay him 30,000 to 60,000 marks per month. He refused every one of these offers. Some may say that perhaps he wanted still more. But if he knew that the day of judgment was close at hand, he also knew that before then, if ever, was the sunshiny day on which to make his hay. A more auspicious time he could never hope to see again.—Let us add, once more, that he never charged admission to any of Hans's performances, although there were many who were anxious to see the horse, and many enthusiasts had come from a great distance. And finally, he was an old man, unmarried and entirely alone, a property owner, but a man whose wants were few and very simple—and his Hans was almost his sole companion. Is it possible that such a man, one who had all the pride of gentle birth, would become a trickster in his old age, all for the love of money?

The unreliability of Mr. von Osten's signs is good proof of their involuntary nature. Anyone who had seen him work with the horse could not have helped noticing that he certainly did not have complete control over the animal, and was not able, at a given moment, to make Hans perform a certain feat, as would have been the case if the process had been one of "training". Again and again Hans failed to make the right count. Before a large audience, one time, it took four tests to get him to tap properly up to 20, and in all four I could note clearly that it was Mr. von Osten who, by his involuntary premature movements, was the innocent cause of the failure. On another occasion, after Hans had done some beautiful work in fractions, in the presence of a large number of spectators, the master asked him the simple question: "Where is the numerator in a fraction?"—The answer was first: "to the left", and then, after a severe reprimand: "down" (below), and finally: "up" (above). He often made just such incorrect movements of the head. In the color-selecting tests the average of error was quite unpredictable. With an equal number of tests, on one day, half would be successful, on another, four fifths, on a third, one-tenth. Often Hans appeared to be "indisposed" for days at a time. The color tests would often end in expressions of rage on the part of Mr. von Osten and in consequence Hans would become startled and would then storm about the courtyard so that it was dangerous to try to approach him. Some may object that all this was mere comedy and that possibly Mr. von Osten prevented some of the tests from turning out successfully. But this objection is to be met by the statement that very often failure would occur just when it was particularly desirable to have the tests appear in a favorable light before a large and enthusiastic assemblage of visitors. After such failures he would be downcast on account of Hans's contrariness. It is also significant that Mr. von Osten's percentage of error, corresponds very closely with my percentage of error in the "non-voluntary" tests, (page 84f.), whereas he never was able to obtain the errorless results which I obtained in my "voluntary" experiments.

But we must be careful not to confuse non-voluntary movement and lack of knowledge of the movement. And again we must distinguish between knowledge of the grosser and the finer signals. Mr. von Osten was aware of the grosser movements, and talked quite freely concerning them, but in so doing, showed that he was quite unaware of their true function. He undertook to show us what we already knew—that, when he remained standing perfectly erect, he could elicit no sort of response from Hans. Furthermore, that whenever he continued to bend forward, Hans would always respond incorrectly and with very high numbers. He knew, also, that Hans was distracted in his operations every time the questioner resumed the erect posture while the tapping was in progress. This he demonstrated to us on one occasion in the following manner. He said to Hans: "You are to count to 7; I will stand erect at 5". He repeated the test five times, and each time Hans stopped tapping when the master raised his body. Several such tests resulted in the same way. Mr. von Osten, however, believed this to be a caprice of the horse and at first declared that he would yet be able to eliminate it, but later became resigned to it as an irremediable evil. Mr. von Osten was also aware that the questioner ought not move while the horse was approaching a colored cloth, and cautioned me in regard to it, though I had already noted as much. And finally, he also knew what influence his calls had while the horse was selecting the cloth, and he told me that it was of great assistance to Hans to be admonished frequently, since thus his attention was brought to bear upon the proper cloth. Yet, when we requested Mr. von Osten to desist calling, since he was thereby influencing the horse in the choice of the cloth, he answered: " Why that's just what I wish to do! "— But though the statement that he was aware of the nature of these grosser signs is thus seen to be true, it by no means necessarily implies that he had purposely trained the animal to respond to them. In these observations of his he had builded better than he knew—he evidently had no notion of their scientific significance. But the same thing might happen to those who were supposed to be somewhat less naïve, as is shown by the experience of Mr. Schillings, who quite unconsciously, for many months had been giving not only the finer, but also the grosser signs, and never guessed the true nature of affairs until I explained it to him. Nor was it an easy matter for me to get at the facts involved in the process, although it now all appears so very simple.

On the other hand, it is also true that Mr. von Osten knew nothing whatever of the finer, more minute signals, such as the final jerk, the head-movement upward, downward, etc., and it is difficult to conceive how he might have gained any knowledge of them. We might perhaps conceive of four possible sources. He might have come upon them by chance. But it is extremely improbable that in the million of possible forms of signaling he should have hit upon those that at the same time represent the natural expressive movements. Or he might have derived a knowledge of them through a study of the pertinent literature. I have searched diligently for such a source, in both the old and the modern literature, but in vain. From the sixteenth century on, there is a series of accounts of horses that were able to spell and to solve problems in arithmetic, and the reports on learned dogs go back even to the time

of Justinian, in the middle of the sixth century.[107]   All
of these animals were kept for purpose of speculation and
were exhibited for pecuniary reasons only.   Nor does one
read that any person could work with these animals off-
hand, which was the characteristic feature of the Osten
horse.*   In many cases we find mention made of the

* There is only one, and I believe it is only a seeming exception
to be found in the literature on the subject.   We are told that
about the year 1840 a French revenue official named Léonard had two
hunting dogs that, besides other things, were able to play at dominoes,
and this not only with their master, but with anyone and without the
master's assistance.   The owner had educated them simply for the fun
of it, and not for pecuniary gain.   This statement is made by both
writers who, apparently independently of one another, have discussed
the case, Youatt [108] and de Tarade.[109]   De Tarade himself played
with them, and gives directions how to teach dogs to play the game.
But his exposition is so naïve, and even ridiculous, for those who know
anything about the subject, that we do not believe it necessary to attempt a detailed refutation.   Youatt never saw the animals.   But he
tells us that not only the dog's partner, but also the master, sat at the
game.   Youatt's assertion, however, that "not the slightest intimation
could have been given by Mr. Leonard to the dog," but that the animal
carried on the game by means of its own observation and calculation,
appears to me a rather bold statement.   After my own experience with
dogs, I firmly believe this to have been impossible.   Hachet-Souplet,[110]
who shares my conviction, explains the matter as follows: the dog
would simply place a domino having the number of eyes named by his
partner, thus the 6 adjacent to the 6, the 3 to the 3, etc.   But even so
a great deal would have to be attributed to the dog, (although in that
case real counting would by no means be absolutely necessary, for an
association between the number term and the total picture of the corresponding group of eyes would suffice.)   But we must note that neither
of the writers mentions that the numbers were always called aloud by
the partner.   After the failure of the experiments of Sir John Lubbock,[111] we must doubt very much if a dog is able to match one domino
with another having the same number of eyes.   We are therefore inclined to believe that this dog continually received signs from its master.
These signs probably were visual, perhaps also auditory, and they were
ϳy no means involuntary.   For in a book on the training of animals,

signs to which the animals reacted. Thus for the beginning or stopping of the animal's scraping or tapping, the signals were respectively raising and lowering of the eyes on the part of the trainer,[113] lowering and raising of the whip [114] or of the arm, stepping forward and backward,[115] and as a closing signal a slight bending forward.[116] The signals for beginning and ceasing to bark in the case of dogs, were the trainer's commands to " speak ", and, at the same time, his looking at the dog, and then looking away for a closing sign; [117] or a mouth-movement on the part of the trainer and then a withdrawing of the left hand which had been resting on the hip.[118] Among the signals for nodding and shaking the head we find the following mentioned: raising and lowering the hand or arm [119] or the whip; [120] a movement of the hand toward the horse's nose, as a signal for nodding, and an arm-movement as a signal for shaking the head.[121]   For this last, we find recommended also a slight breathing upon the animal,[122] and—in the case of dogs—a mouth-movement simulating blowing, or a turn of the fingers.[123] (We will not dwell upon the many signals for selecting objects, which are mentioned, since we have already discussed this point on page 230f).   In all these instances it is plain that we have to do with purely voluntary and

which Léonard, the owner of the dogs, has published, and in which he describes minutely the method by which they had been trained in their various accomplishments, he does not mention with so much as a syllable the game of dominoes, a thing which he certainly would have dwelt upon, if he had believed in the animals' power of independent thought. He would not have remained silent concerning this greatest —though only apparent—achievement of his educational endeavors. But his whole book is evidence that he was too wise to have thus deceived himself, and our only alternative is to believe that he was playing a joke on his credulous admirers.

" artificial " signals.   The only example of involuntary
signs which Mr. von Osten could have found in literature,
was that of Huggins's dog, which need not be considered
here, since, as was said on page 177, the really effective
signs in that case were not discovered.   A third means by
which Mr. von Osten might have gained a knowledge of
the involuntary, natural expressive signs, would have
been by observing others.   If he had had opportunity of
observing another von Osten and another Hans, he might
have gotten at the secret.   But since this was not the
case, this possibility vanishes.   A fourth possibility is
self-observation.   We would then have to assume that
Mr. von Osten at first really tried to educate the horse
to think, but soon recognized the fruitlessness of such an
attempt.   At the same time, he then would have noticed
his own involuntary movements and their effect upon the
horse, and having noted them, voluntarily reduced their
extent and utilized them in the training process.   But
here also there is much that militates against this assumption when we consider how great is the difficulty of consciously refining movements which at first were rather
coarse, unless it be by the adjustment of the proper degree of concentration of attention, a subtlety of method
of which we could hardly believed Mr. von Osten capable.
We must remember, also, that in the first publication regarding Hans which, by the way, marks the beginning
of his career, (" Das lesende und rechnende Pferd," by
Major-General E. Zobel, in the " Weltspiegel " of July 7,
1904), we may read the following : " He (Mr. von Osten)
is always willing to have the horse undergo an examination on the part of a stranger, and promises that after
Hans has become fairly well acquainted he will display
the same degree of efficiency as he displays with the mas-

ter, himself. This occurred at a time when Mr. Schillings, the man who was destined to prove the truth of the statement, had not yet appeared on the scene. How was Mr. von Osten to know beforehand that every questioner, who might appear, would execute the same movements that he himself had used? We would recall also that not one in the great multitude of persons who worked successfully with the horse in the absence of Mr. von Osten, had noticed, even in the slightest measure, any of these movements in themselves. The position and repute of these persons vouches for their veracity,—among them were the writer of the article just mentioned, the Count zu Castell, Count Matuschka, Count von Eickstedt-Peterswaldt, General Köring, Dr. Sander, Mr. H. Suermondt and Mr. H. von Tepper-Laski. Some of these gentlemen were quite unwilling to believe that they executed such movements. This happened in the case of Mr. von Tepper-Laski, who had visited Hans ten times and who had, during the course of these visits, frequently worked alone with the horse and had received correct responses. Count Eickstedt, too, although he was one of those who had been made acquainted with the nature of the movements involved before being allowed to visit the horse, was unable to note them either in his observation of Mr. von Osten, or of himself, when, in compliance with his own wish, he was left alone with Hans. Nor did any of the laboratory subjects, some of whom were well trained in introspection, discover the true nature of affairs. They were thoroughly astonished when the facts of the case were explained to them. And I, also, as was mentioned on page 100, did not become aware of my own movements, until I had noted those of Mr. von Osten. In fine, everything would indicate that we have here not an intention to deceive the public, but a case of pure self-deception.*

This self-deception is easily understood when we consider the two predominent characteristics of the man: the pedantry of the pedagogue, and his proneness to be possessed by a single idea, which is a peculiarity of those of an inventive turn of mind. Adhering closely to a preformed plan, he carefully and narrowly circumscribed the scope and order of instruction. He would not go on to the number 5 if he were not thoroughly convinced that the 4 had been completely mastered, nor would he go on to a more difficult problem in multiplication, until he felt certain that Hans was entirely proficient in the problems of the simpler sort. If he had ever put a question to Hans before its regular order, he would have discovered, to his amazement, that there really existed no difficulties for Hans, and also that the horse really required no appreciable time to acquire new material. Mr. von Osten would have had a like experience if he had asked Hans concerning the value of Chinese coins or the logarithm of 1000. However, he never did anything of the kind, but always adhered closely to his plan. He required the questioner to say: " 2 and 2 ", and never " 2 plus 2 ". Nor were capitals or Latin script to be used in the written material. And if upon request he did so, he did it, without faith in the result, and hence there was failure.

---

* P. Wasmann, S. J. in the third edition of his book, " Instinkt und Intelligenz im Tierreich " (Freiburg, Herder, 1905), discusses the case of Hans and quotes from a letter I wrote him concerning the matter. In the quotation an error has crept in, which I would here correct. The statement is ascribed to me that " Hans differs from other horses only in his extraordinary power of observation, an unintentional by-product of intentional training," whereas in my letter I said : " unintentional by-product of intentional education."

And so he declared that "if you use Latin script Hans becomes confused and will be out of sorts for several weeks thereafter." Mr. von Osten is, and ever will remain, the schoolmaster, and will never become the psychologist, the "soul-vivisectionist". Who would work a child with such puzzling questions? and Hans was to him like a child. Thus the old man believed himself to be a witness of a continuous, organic development of the animal soul—a development which in reality had no other existence than in his own imagination.

Added to this pedantry was an extraordinary uncritical attitude of mind, induced by his obsession by one favorite idea, which blinded him to all objections. He met objectionable observations on the part of others in one of two ways. One method was by attributing to Hans certain remarkable qualities, such as an extraordinary keenness of hearing and a wonderful power of memory, or again, certain defects, such as moodiness and stubbornness,—which as a matter of fact, were only so many back-doors by which he might escape from the necessity of offering adequate explanations. When Hans was able to give off-hand a gentleman's name which he had heard years before, it was called a case of extraordinary memory. When the horse insisted that 2 times 2 was 5, he maintained that it was an example of animal stubbornness. There was still a simpler method of overcoming inconvenient objections and that was by ignoring them altogether. The number 1, the simplest and most fundamental in the system of numbers, was one of the most difficult for Hans. (Page 67f.). Mr. von Osten was aware of this, but thought little of it. During the very first visit of Professor Stumpf, Mr. von Osten asked the horse: "By how much must you increase the numerator of the fraction $\frac{7}{8}$, in order to get a whole number?" Hans repeatedly answered incorrectly and always tapped numbers that were too great. The same question was then asked concerning the fraction $\frac{5}{8}$, and immediately there was a correct response, (the favorite number 3). Mr. von Osten said very naïvely: "In the case of the difference of 1, he always goes wrong. It was just what I expected." Mr. von Osten still relates that the distinction between right and left created far greater difficulty for Hans than all of the work in fractions, and that even to-day it is not thoroughly established; also, that the selection of colored cloths is often a failure still, although it was one of the first things in which he was given instruction. It appears never to have dawned upon Mr. von Osten that the arts in which Hans seemed to excel, also formed the standing repertoire of so many trained horses, regarding whom it was well-known that they owed all of their cleverness to the training given them by their masters. This fact alone should have induced him to make some form of critical investigation.

When Hans suddenly became a celebrity, and he, himself, the object of an enthusiastic following, the whole affair evidently took Mr. von Osten off his feet. Strangers took the further instruction of the horse in charge, and the rate and degree of Hans's progress became disconcerting. One day it came to pass that the horse even understood French, and the old gentleman, whose apostolic exterior had always exerted a high degree of suggestion upon his admirers, in turn fell captive to the spell of retroactive mass-suggestion. He no longer was uneasy concerning the most glaring kinds of failure. On one occasion he even insisted upon the completion of a series of tests in which procedure was "without knowledge", which promised no results whatever. " The animal's stubbornness must be broken," he commented. On the other hand, he regarded every criticism as a form of personal insult. And once he showed a member of the committee of the Society for the Protection of Animals the door, because the man, without having looked at his watch, wanted to show it to Hans and ask him the time. Many other critics had similar experiences.

Summarizing the remarks of this chapter, our judgment must be as follows: It is in the highest degree improbable that Mr. von Osten purposely trained the horse to respond to certain cues. It is also improbable that he knew that in every test he was giving signals, (although I can form no judgment concerning what happened after the publication of the latest report). To assume the contrary would land us in the midst of insoluble contradictions of the many ascertained facts in the case. The explanation here essayed, however, should prevent that. To be sure, we, must then reckon with curious inner contradictions in Mr. von Osten's character. But such contradictions are to be found, upon earnest analysis, in nearly every human character. And Mr. von Osten may say with the poet: " Ich bin kein ausgeklügelt Buch. Ich bin ein Mensch mit seinem Widerspruch."

CONCLUSION

If we would make a brief summary of the status of Mr. von Osten's horse in the light of these investigations and try to understand what is the bearing upon the question of animal psychology in general, we may make the following statements.

Hans's accomplishments are founded first upon a one-sided development of the power of perceiving the slightest movements of the questioner, secondly upon the intense and continued, but equally one-sided, power of attention, and lastly upon a rather limited memory, by means of which the animal is able to associate perceptions of movement with a small number of movements of its own which have become thoroughly habitual.

The horse's ability to perceive movements greatly exceeds that of the average man. This superiority is probably due to a different constitution of the retina, and perhaps also of the brain.

Only a diminshingly small number of auditory stimuli are involved.

All conclusions with regard to the presence of emotional reactions, such as stubbornness, etc., have been shown to be without warrant. With regard to the emotional life we are justified in concluding from the behavior of the horse, that the desire for food is the only effective spring to action.

The gradual formation of the associations mentioned above, between the perception of movement and the movements of the horse himself, is in all probability not to be regarded as the result of a training-process, but as an unintentional by-product of an unsuccessful attempt at real education, which, though in no sense a training-process, still produced results equivalent to those of such a process.

All higher psychic processes which find expression in the horse's behavior, are those of the questioner. His relationship to the horse is brought about almost wholly by involuntary movements of the most minute kind. The interrelation existing between ideas having a high degree of affective coloring and the musculature of the body, (which is brought to light in this process), is by no means a novel fact for us. Nevertheless, it is possible that this case may be of no small value, on account of the great difficulties which are usually met in the attempt to establish experimentally the more delicate details in this field.

And, returning to the considerations of the first chapter, if we ask what contributions does this case make toward a solution of the problem of animal consciousness, we may state the following: The proof which was expected by so many, that animals possess the power of thought, was not furnished by Hans. He has served to weaken, rather than strengthen, the position of these enthusiasts. But we must generalize this negative conclusion of ours with care,—for Hans cannot without further qualification be regarded as normal. Hans is a domesticated animal. It is possible (though the opposite is usually assumed), that our animals have suffered in the development of their mental life, as a result of the process of domestication. To be sure, in some respects they have become more specialized than their wild kin, (e. g., our hunting dogs), and in their habits they have become adapted largely to suit our needs. This latter is shown by all the anecdotes concerning " clever " dogs, horses, etc. But with the loss of their freedom they have also gradually been deprived of the urgent need of self-preservation and of the preservation of their species, and thus lack one of the greatest forces that make for psychic development. And often their artificial selection and culture has been with a view to the development of muscle and sinew, fat and wool, all at the expense of brain development.* Our horses are, as a rule, sentenced to an especially dull mode of life. Chained in stalls (and usually dark stalls at that,) during three-fourths of their lives, and more than any other domestic animal, enslaved for thousands of years by reins and whip, they have become estranged from their natural impulses, and owing to continued confinement they may perhaps have suffered even in their sensory life. A gregarious animal, yet kept constantly in isolation, intended by nature to range over vast areas, yet confined to his narrow courtyard, and deprived of opportunity for sexual activity,—he has been forced by a process of education to develop along lines quite opposite to his native characteristics. Nevertheless, I believe that it is very doubtful if it would have been possible by other methods, even, to call forth in the horse the ability to think. Presumably, however, it might be possible, under conditions and with methods of instruction more in accord with the life-needs of the horse, to awaken in a fuller measure those mental activities which would be called into play to meet those needs.

---

* Buffon,[124] the great naturalist, expresses himself not less pessimistically in his own brilliant manner : " Un animal domestique est un esclave dont on s'amuse, dont on se sert, dont on abuse, qu'on altère, qu'on dépaïse et que l'on dénature."

Though our investigations do not give support to the fantastic acounts of animal intelligence given by Brehms, they by no means warrant a return to Descartes and his theory of the animal-machine (as is advocated by a number of over-critical investigators). We cannot deny the validity of conclusions from analogy without denying at the same time the possibility of an animal psychology—indeed of all psychology. And all such conclusions indicate that the lower forms possess the power of sense-perception, that they, like us, presumably have at their disposal certain images, and that their psychic life is to a large extent also constituted of mere image-associations, and that they too, learn by experience. Also that they are susceptible to feelings of pleasure and of pain and also to emotions, as jealousy, fear, etc., though these may be only of the kind which have a direct relation to their life-needs. We are in no position to deny *a priori* the possibility of traces of conceptual thought in those forms nearest man in the scale—whether living in their natural manner or under artificial conditions. And even less so since the final word has not yet been spoken regarding the nature of conceptual thinking itself. All that is certain is that nothing of the kind has been proven to occur in the lower forms, and that as yet not even a suitable method of discovering its existence has been suggested. But the community of those elementary processes of mental life which we have mentioned above is in itself enough to connect the life of the lower forms with ours, and imposes upon us the duty of regarding them not as objects for exploitation and mistreatment, but as worthy of rational care and affection.

SUPPLEMENTS

SUPPLEMENT I

MR. VON OSTEN'S METHOD OF INSTRUCTION

[By C. Stumpf]

The following is a report of the account, which Mr. von Osten gave Professor Schumann and me, of the method which he had used in the instruction of the horse, and which was illustrated by actual demonstrations. I cannot testify, of course, that Mr. von Osten really did adhere to this method throughout the four years in which he tutored the horse, but I will say that I have several good reasons for believing that it was impossible for him to have trumped up this make-believe scheme afterward, merely to mislead us. Among the reasons are the following: He was always ready to give a detailed explanation of any question which we might interpose; the written statements of Major von Keller, who has known Mr. von Osten for a period of fifteen years; the testimony of General Zobel, who became acquainted with the whole process fully a year before any public exhibitions were given; the accounts given by the tenants in Mr. von Osten's house, who for years saw the process of instruction going on in the courtyard of the apartment building,—according to their account his intercourse with the horse was like that with a child at school,—he made much use of the apparatus and never did they notice any-thing like an habituation to respond to certain signals; and finally the appearance of the apparatus itself—some of which could not be bought at second hand—was most convincing.

The apparatus used for the work in arithmetic consisted mainly of a set of large wooden pins, a set of smaller ones (such as are to be had in toy-shops), a counting-machine, such as is commonly used in the schools, a chart upon which were pasted the numbers from 1 to 100, and finally the digits, cut large and in brass and suspended from a string. For the work in reading Mr. von Osten used the chart shown in the frontispiece of this book. Here we have the letters of the alphabet in small German script with numbers written below which serve to indi-cate the row, and what place in that row, the letters occupy. For tones, a small, child's organ was used with the diatonic scale C^1 to C^2, and for instruction in colors, a number of colored cloths were used.

The work in arithmetic began by placing a single wooden pin in front of Hans and then commanding him: "Raise the foot!—One!" Here we must assume that the horse had learned to respond to the command to raise the foot during the preceding period, when tapping in general had been taught. In order to get the horse to learn that he was to give only one tap, Mr. von Osten tried to control the tapping by means of holding the ani-mal's foot, just as a teacher tries to aid a pupil in learning to write by guiding his hand. He repeated this exercise so often that finally the single tap was made. And al-ways the right foot was insisted upon. Bread and carrots were the constant rewards.

Two of the pins were now set up and the command given: " Raise the foot!—One, two! " Mr. von Osten again aided the establishment of the proper association by using his hand as before. At the same time the two pins were pointed out, and the order was always without exception from left to right. Gradually it became unnecessary to touch the foot or to point to the pins, and instead the question was introduced: " How many are there? ", in order that the horse should become accustomed to these words as an invitation to give the taps when he saw the wooden pins before him.

Then three pins were taken and the words " one, two, three " were spoken, and so on. In naming a number the preceding ones were always named along with it, in order that the normal order might thus be learned at the same time. Later the number alone, without the preceding ones, sufficed to elicit the proper number of taps. The last word of the series thus becomes characteristic of the series as a whole. It differs from all the others, and thus becomes the sign for the whole series of numbers thus named, each of which arises as a memory image at the proper place in the series and is accompanied by a tap of the foot. Thus, Mr. von Osten at any rate had accounted to himself for his success.

But Hans was not to acquire merely this relatively mechanical process of counting (hardly to be called counting), but he was to acquire also some meaning content for the number terms. For this purpose everything depended upon the concept " and ". Only he who can grasp its meaning will be able to understand a number. 2 is 1 *and* 1, 3 is 2 *and* 1. Mr. von Osten had someone hold a large cloth before the horse, where the wooden pins usually were placed. He then had the cloth taken up and he would pronounce emphatically the word "and". After this had been done a number of times, he put up two of the pins and obscured them by the cloth. The cloth was again raised and the word "and" pronounced. Then Hans, as a result of his previous instruction (so Mr. von Osten thought) would give two taps at sight of the pins. The thing was repeated with three pins, then with one, and so on, and the horse would always execute the proper number of taps.

Now, five pins were set up, the three to the right being covered by the cloth. The horse tapped twice and Mr. von Osten said "two". Then the cloth was raised, Hans gave three further taps, and Mr. von Osten said "and three" with emphasis.

In this simple manner he tried to get the horse to understand that the three belongs to the two, and that both together make five. The image of the five pins as it was known from previous experience, was to be associated with the combined groups of two and three, and conversely, it was to be reproduced when these groups were presented. Later the cloth and pins were omitted and the question was asked: "How much is two and three?". The horse tapped five times. It had learned how to add. Still this could be regarded only as a mechanical process, if the horse were able to add only those numbers which had been presented together one or more times in the manner just described. And so long as we remained within the first decade, we could get twenty-five binary combinations whose sum does not exceed 10 (counting inverted orders we would have forty-five binary permutations),—all of which might have been practised separately. But as a matter of fact, Mr. von Osten did not take this course, for as he himself says, he allowed Hans to discover a great deal for himself. " Hans had to develop the multiplication table for himself."—With larger numbers and more addends, the number of combinations becomes so great that there can be no doubt they were not practised separately.

Since, after all this preliminary instruction, Hans really began to give solutions of new problems, the master believed that this was proof that he had succeeded in inculcating the inner meaning of the number concepts, and not merely an external association of memory images with certain movement responses. But he always remained within the sphere of the ideas thus developed, and adhered closely to the customary vocabulary and its usage. Every new concept, each additional word was explained anew.

It would not be legitimate to condemn the whole procedure from the very beginning on the ground of the horse's lack of knowledge of language or of its use. It was Mr. von Osten's aim to convey to the horse an understanding of the language, by means of sense-presentations, adequate to give rise to the proper sense-perceptions. Helen Keller and other blind deaf-mutes have been educated to an understanding of the language without the aid of vision and hearing. They have come to it through the sense of touch alone. Everything depends upon whether or not the predisposition for it is present. And it was quite rational that Mr. von Osten should have chosen counting and arithmetical calculation as the processes by which to make his attack upon the animal mind, for as a matter of fact, nowhere else is it so easy to bridge the gap between perception and conception and nowhere else can the sign of success or failure be perceived so readily as in the handling of numbers. It is unfortunate, however, that he did not utilize these same signs for purposes of counter-testing also, as, for instance, by inquiring for the cube root of 729. But he was prevented from doing this by his close adherence to his pedagogical principle and by his unquestioning faith in the soundness of the entire procedure.

In teaching multiplication the counting machine was used. Two of the ten balls on one of the rods were pushed far to the left, thus: oo. " How many are there? " Two taps. " Very well. That is once two." Another group of two was pushed to the left, at a short interval from the first group, thus: oo oo. " How many times two balls are there? " was asked, with a decided movement of the hand toward the two groups. Two taps. " How many, therefore, are two times two? " Four taps.

The horse was supposed to learn the meaning of the word " times " by means of the spatial separation of the groups; he was to be taught to notice and to count the groups, and also the number of units in a single group. Three times two then meant three groups with two units in each group. The horse was supposedly aided by the following factors: the relative nearness of the units belonging to one group, as over against the space interval between the groups themselves; also that the groups were pointed out as wholes in connection with the emphatic enunciation of the words ' once, ' twice, etc.; and finally the touching and raising of the horse's foot by means of the hand until all the desired associations of the ideas with one another and with the corresponding tapping movements were quite perfect.

Subtraction was taught in the following manner. Five pins were set up; the horse tapped five times. Mr. von

Osten then removed two of them and said emphatically:
" I take away, — minus. " How many are still standing? " The horse tapped three times. Here, too, there
was at first some assistance by means of the hand to get
the tapping.

In division four balls were first pushed to the left end
of the rod, thus: oooo. " How many balls are there to
the left? " Four taps. They were now divided into two
pairs, thus: oo oo. Pointing to the units of one group,
the teacher asks: " There are always how many in the
group? " Two taps. Three groups were formed, thus:
oo oo oo. " There are now how many balls to the left? "
Six taps. " And there are always how many in each
group? ", (pointing at them). Two taps. " And how
often is two contained in six? ", (pointing to the groups
consecutively). Three taps, etc.

The ideas of ' part ', of ' whole ', and of ' being contained ' were illustrated by means of a chalk line which
was interrupted in one or more places by erasure.

In all these operations Mr. von Osten adhered strictly
to the rule, and required others to do so too, that the number upon which the operation was performed, must be
mentioned first. Thus, one was not to say, " take 3 away
from 7 ", but " from 7 take away 3." Otherwise, he believed, Hans would become easily confused. Also one
was not allowed to say " to multiply ", but to " take " a
certain number so many " times ". He, himself, never
departed from this practice.

We will not go into the details of the method by which
Hans was taught the meaning of the number signs, of the
signs of operation, of the numbers above 10, or the significance of " digits ", " tens ", etc. Only this,—when in
problems in addition the sum was greater than 10, the 10

was first tapped and then the remainder of the number added to the 10. Thus: " You are to add 9 and 5. How much must you add to the 9 to have 10?" One tap. " But now, you were to add not merely 1, but 5; how much have you still to add to the 10?"—Four taps. In like manner, whenever the addends were below 20 or 30 and the sum above 20 or 30, Mr. von Osten would ask for the 20 or 30 taps first. He thought that he was thus giving his pupil an ever firmer grasp upon the principle of the structure of our number system, in which all higher numbers are constituted of tens and digits. For the same reason he used at first, instead of the words ' eleven ' and ' twelve ' (' elf ' and ' zwölf ' in the German), expressions which in English might be rendered as ' one-teen ' and ' two-teen ' (' einzehn ' and ' zweizehn ' in the German) ; and only later, after the animal had seemingly mastered the meaning in question, did Mr. von Osten replace them by the usual forms.

All this was beautifully conceived and might perhaps form the basis for the instruction of primitive races. But it is of immediate interest for us only because it enables us to better understand the origin of the conviction under which Mr. von Osten and his followers labored.

SUPPLEMENT II

THE REPORT OF SEPTEMBER 12, 1904

" THE undersigned came together for the purpose of investigating the question whether or not there is involved in the feats of the horse of Mr. von Osten anything of the nature of tricks, that is, intentional influence or aid, on the part of the questioner. After a careful investigation they are unanimously agreed that such signs are out of the question under the conditions which were maintained during this investigation. This decision in no wise takes into account the character of the men exhibiting the horse, and who are known to most of the undersigned. In spite of the most attentive observation, nothing in the way of movements or other forms of expression which might have served as a sign, could be discovered. In order to obviate involuntary movements on the part of those present, one series of tests was made with only Mr. Busch present. Among these tests were some in which, according to his professional judgment, the possibility of tricks of the sort commonly used in training, was excluded. Another series of tests was made in such a way that the correct answers to the questions which Mr. von Osten put to the horse, were unknown to the ·questioner. From previous observation the greater number of the undersigned also know of a large number of cases in which, during the absence of Mr. von Osten and Mr. Schillings, other persons were likewise able to obtain correct responses from the horse. Among these were some cases in which the questioner did not know the correct solution of the problem or was mistaken about it.   And lastly, several of the undersigned have become acquainted with the method which Mr. von Osten used, which has little in common with methods of training, and is patterned after the instruction given in the elementary schools.   As a result of these observations the undersigned are of the opinion that unintentional signs of the kind which are at present familiar, are likewise excluded. They are unanimously agreed that this much is certain: This is a case which appears in principle to differ from any hitherto discovered, and has nothing in common with training, in the usual sense of that word, and therefore is worthy of a serious and incisive investigation.

BERLIN, September 12, 1904.

> PAUL BUSCH, Circus-manager.
> OTTO, COUNT ZU CASTELL-RÜDENHAUSEN.
> DR. A. GRABOW, member of the schoolboard, retired.
> ROBERT HAHN, Teacher, Municipal schools.
> DR. LUDWIG HECK, Director of the Zoölogical Garden.
> DR. OSCAR HEINROTH, Assistant in the Berlin Zoölogical Garden.
> DR. RICHARD KANDT.
> MAJOR F. W. VON KELLER, retired.
> MAJOR-GENERAL TH. KÖRING, retired.
> DR. MIESSNER, Assistant in the Royal Veterinary College.
> PROF. NAGEL, Head of the department of sense-physiology in the Physiological Institute of the University of Berlin.
> PROF. C. STUMPF, Director of the Psychological Institute, Member of the Academy of Sciences.
> HENRY SUERMONDT."

SUPPLEMENT III

AN ABSTRACT FROM THE RECORDS OF THE SEPTEMBER-COMMISSION *

THE important meetings occurred on the 11th and 12th of September and both of them extended over four hours. The greatest difficulty was occasioned by the condition laid down by Mr. von Osten: that we were to work without him from the very beginning. In a certain sense this condition had been met once before when Mr. Schillings appeared upon the scene, a man whose fairness ought to be doubted by none. He came utterly skeptical, and yet in the course of a week he learned to handle the horse and received responses regularly. However, since the public had begun to doubt Mr. Schillings also, another person had to attempt the rôle of questioner. Count zu Castell tried to do this and practised for some days before the meetings, but his success—although of no small moment—was not great enough to be convincing.

In apprising Mr. von Osten of this fact we caused a veritable catastrophe. He declared in a most decisive manner that he would have to insist upon the condition

* A few days after the 12th of September I made the present abstract from the original records af the Commission, which I have here abbreviated somewhat. (See page 8). Referring once more to the misunderstanding mentioned on page 3, I would say that the closing sentence of the report is here re-given literally as it then appeared. C. St.

he had imposed, since the public demanded it, and he could never assist in any tests, until he had been cleared of the suspicion of having descended to the use of tricks. If it should take weeks to accustom the horse to a new questioner, there would be no alternative but to wait that length of time.

A happy circumstance helped us out of our difficulty. We had chanced in our discussion to mention the experience of Dr. Miessner, a member of the commission, who on the day before had gone to witness an exhibition of the mare " Clever Rosa ", and who believed that he had succeeded in discovering the tricks involved. There was a sudden change in Mr. von Osten's attitude. He expressed his willingness to undergo the most stringent examination and agreed to anything in the way of conditions of control, challenging even the proven ability of Dr. Miessner. " I have neither whip nor rod, as had the man in the exhibition, and agree to any precautionary measures you may care to take."

After he had gone, the commission decided to ask him to have the horse perform one of the more common, simple, feats. They were going to watch him very closely. Different members were assigned the task of attending to different parts of his body (head, eyes, right hand, left hand, etc.) while Mr. Busch, since he was the most proficient in the detection of tricks, was to regard the total behavior of the man.

The exhibitions included the indication of the day of the week by means of taps, the day just past, the day ahead, its date, arithmetical problems, and the counting of rings strung upon a rod. Messrs. Grabow and Hahn interpolated a few tests themselves, in which they did the questioning. All tests were successful.

Mr. von Osten withdrew, and in comparison of notes which followed, Mr. Busch, as well as all the others, declared that they had discovered nothing of the nature of a visible sign. Mr. Busch said that he had also kept an eye on the spectators and had noticed nothing there. Nevertheless, he desired to see Mr. von Osten go through one series with no one else but himself (Busch) present.

This was done, and on this occasion a number of tests were made in the recognition of colored cloths. The horse was required to indicate, by tapping, the place in the series which the cloth occupied and was then asked to bring the green or the red, as the case might be, in his mouth. Furthermore, he was asked to approach that one of the five gentlemen standing at a distance, whose photograph had been shown him. Then he was requested to spell the words " Rat " and " Busch " according to the method which he had been taught. Nearly all of these tests were likewise successful.

In the conference which followed, Mr. Busch again declared that he had noticed no trace of a sign; he maintained that, in the selecting of colored cloths (especially when they were placed so closely together) and in the approach toward a person, there was no possibility whatever that some trick was being used.

During the session of September 12th, Mr. von Osten agreed to two sets of experiments.

1. Another man was to put the question to the horse. Mr. von Osten himself was to stand, back to back to the questioner and to bend forward, so that he was effectually hidden from the horse's view, yet could, by means of occasional calls, make his presence known to the animal. The assumption was that it would be conducive to success if the horse knew that the master was present and

was awaiting the answer, and yet at the same time the possibility of receiving a sign was obviated.

2. Another man in Mr. von Osten's absence was to ask the horse to tap a certain number. Then the questioner was to leave, and Mr. von Osten, returning, was to ask the horse to perform some arithmetical process with the number which was thus unknown to the master. Mr. von Osten said that he thought that this method was somewhat risky, since the horse would be aware that he, Mr. von Osten, did not know the number, and might therefore be in a humor to play some prank.

The questions of the first sort were answered with but very few errors. Mr. Hahn and Count zu Castell asked simple questions in arithmetic. When Mr. von Osten withdrew into the stable, the count put several other problems, among them the counting of persons and of windows, all of which were solved correctly.

Between the first and second series of tests the following experiments were interpolated. The names of six members of the commission were written upon six slates respectively, which were then suspended from a string. Mr. von Osten pointed to one of the men and asked: " On which of the slates is this gentleman's name to be found? ". The correct number was tapped in every case. The command to approach the slate in question was also obeyed as a rule, although this was not as uniformly successful as tapping.

In the conference which followed, Mr. Busch declared that the feats appeared inconceivable to him; and again none of the men had noted anything in the way of signs.

Now followed the second series of tests mentioned above. In order to be sure to get the correct responses, Mr. Schillings, who up to this point had not been present at any of the experiments, was asked to put the questions to the horse. Mr. von Osten went into the house, accompanied by a member of the commission. And again, Mr. Schillings would go out before the second part of the test, without having met Mr. von Osten.

Five tests were made in this way. They were not attended by such amazing success as were the preceding ones, but nevertheless the results were surprising. The horse nearly always repeated the number itself, instead of performing the operation required. Since, however, Mr. Schillings, owing to a misunderstanding, had, in the first two cases, said to the horse: " You are to repeat this number for Mr. von Osten ", the errors might appear to be a result of this request.

At the final discussion, the result of which was the unanimous declaration which was given for publication, not only the data obtained during these two sessions, but also the earlier experiences of some of the members of the commission were taken into consideration. None of the tests witnessed could be referred to chance or to the use of tricks. Count zu Castell pointed out that in the course of eight days he had elicited forty correct responses from the horse, among them some in regard to which he himself had been momentarily in error. Other members recalled the many instances in previous exhibitions, during which both Mr. Schillings and Mr. von Osten were absent, when questions were put to the horse by others. The commission also had access to a detailed account written by Professor Stumpf on Mr. von Osten's method of instruction, based on the explanations and demonstrations which Mr. von Osten had himself given. As a result of these considerations the commission felt under obligations to give public expression to its conviction. In the report it limited itself, however, to the purely negative side—principally in denying the use of tricks,—and expressed no opinion with regard to the actual genesis of the horse's accomplishments, since it believed that there was great possibility that other factors were involved which ought to be carefully investigated.

SUPPLEMENT IV

THE REPORT OF DECEMBER 9TH, 1904

TOGETHER with Dr. E. von Hornbostel and Mr. O. Pfungst, I have tried during the past few weeks to find an explanation of the accomplishments of the horse 'Hans' by the experimental method. We had access to the horse in the absence of the master and groom. The results are as follows:

The horse failed in his responses whenever the solution of the problem that was given him was unknown to any of those present. For instance, when a written number or the objects to be counted were placed before the horse, but were invisible to everyone else, and especially to the questioner, he failed to respond properly. Therefore he can neither count, nor read, nor solve problems in arithmetic.

The horse failed again whenever he was prevented by means of sufficiently large blinders from seeing the persons, and especially the questioner, to whom the solution was known. He therefore required some sort of visual aid.

These aids need not, however,—and this is the peculiarly interesting feature in the case,—be given intentionally. The proof for this is found in the fact that in the absence of Mr. von Osten the horse gave correct replies to a large number of persons; and to be more specific, Mr. Schillings and later Mr. Pfungst, after working with the horse for a short time, regularly received correct answers, without their being in any way conscious of having given any kind of signal.

So far as I can see, the following explanation is the only one that will comport with these facts. The horse must have learned, in the course of the long period of problem-solving, to attend ever more closely, while tapping, to the slight changes in bodily posture with which the master unconsciously accompanied the steps in his own thought-processes, and to use these as closing signals. The motive for this direction and straining of attention was the regular reward in the form of carrots and bread, which attended it. This unexpected kind of independent activity and the certainty and precision of the perception of minimal movements thus attained, are astounding in the highest degree.

The movements which call forth the horse's reaction, are so extremely slight in the case of Mr. von Osten, that it is easily comprehensible how it was possible that they should escape the notice even of practised observers. Mr. Pfungst, however, whose previous laboratory experience had made him keen in the perception of visual stimuli of slightest duration and extent, succeeded in recognizing in Mr. von Osten the different kinds of movements which were the basis of the various accomplishments of the horse. Furthermore, he succeeded in controlling his own movements, (of which he had hitherto been unconscious), in the presence of the horse, and finally became so proficient that he could replace these unintentional movements by intentional ones. He can now call forth at will all the various reactions of the horse by making the proper kind of voluntary movements, without asking the relevant question or giving any sort of command. But Mr. Pfungst meets with the same success when he does not attend to the movements to be made, but rather focuses, as intently as possible, upon the number desired, since in that case the necessary movement occurs whether he wills it or not. In the near future he will give a special detailed report of his observations, which gives promise of becoming a valuable contribution to the study of involuntary movements. Also he will give an account of our tests and of the mechanism of the various accomplishments of the horse. We must also defer, till then, the disproof of certain seemingly relevant arguments in favor of the horse's power of independent thought.

Some defenders of the view which maintains the horse's rationality may urge that it was only through our experiments that the animal became trained and spoiled in so far as the ability to think is concerned. They are refuted in this, however, by the fact that the horse still continues to solve problems involving decimal fractions and to determine calendar dates for Mr. von Osten, as brilliantly as ever, as is shown by his recent demonstration before a large group of spectators. That these results are now being achieved in a manner essentially different from formerly is nothing but a bare assertion.

On the other hand, now that the possibility has been established that these wonderful results may be obtained in all their complexity by means of intentional signs, many will question whether Mr. Von Osten did not himself train the horse from the very beginning to respond to these signs. No one has the right, however, to charge an old man, who has never had a blemish on his reputation, with having invented a most refined network of lies, if the facts can be explained in a satisfactory manner in some other rational way. And this can be done in this case. For we have seen that there is another alternative, other than the theory that the horse can think or the assumption that tricks have been employed.

And now, aside from the specific results obtained, what is the scientific and philosophic import of the whole affair?—For one thing, the revolution in our conception of the animal mind, which had been hoped for by some, and feared by others, has not taken place. But a conclusion of an opposite character is justified. If such unexampled patience and high pedagogical excellence as was daily brought to bear by Mr. von Osten during the course of four long years, could not bring to light the slightest trace of conceptual thinking, then the old assertion of the philosophers that the lower forms are incapable of such thinking, finds corroboration in the results of these experiments so far as the animal scale up to and including the ungulates is concerned. For this reason the tremendous effort put forth by Mr. von Osten, is not, in spite of the self-deception under which he labors, lost to science. If anyone has the courage to try the experiment with the dog or the ape, the insight which we have now gained will enable him to beware of one source of error which hitherto has not been noticed.

In the face of much misapprehension which has arisen, I wish once more to say emphatically that the committee of September 12th in no wise declared itself to be convinced that the horse had the power of rational thinking. The committee restricted itself entirely to the question whether or not tricks were involved, and, intentionally and rightly referred the positive investigation to a purely scientific court. I would also report that for some time Mr. Schillings has been convinced, by his own observations, of the horse's lack of reason, and when he was apprised of our conclusion in the matter, he embraced it without wavering. I have no intention of taking part in any discussion which may arise in the press as a result of the present report. Unless they wish to confine themselves to mere guesswork, the defenders of other views will not shrink from the task of basing their criticism upon careful methodical experimentation, and they will keep a detailed record of their results day by day; for statements based solely upon memory, without specific report of experimental conditions, prove nothing.

PROF. CARL STUMPF.

December 9th, 1904.

TABLE OF REFERENCES

(The names of the authors of anonymous works are placed in parenthesis.)

1. ZELL, TH. Das rechnende Pferd. Ein Gutachten über den " Klugen Hans " auf Grund eigener Beobachtungen. Berlin, R. Dietze, 1904.

2. FREUND, F. Der "kluge" Hans? Ein Beitrag zur Aufklärung. Berlin, Boll and Pickardt, 1904.

3. HANSEN, F. C. C. and A. Lehmann. Über unwillkürliches Flüstern. Philosophische Studien, edited by W. Wundt, Leipsic, 1895, Vol. 11, pp. 471 ff.

4. SANDEN, S. v. Über Aktivität und Passivität des Reiters und seiner Hülfen. Deutsche hippologische Presse, Berlin, 1896, Jahrg. 12, No. 11, pp. 117 ff. and No. 12, pp. 128 ff.

5. WEYER, E. M. Some Experiments on the Reaction-Time of a Dog. Studies from the Yale Psychological Laboratory, New Haven, Conn., 1895, Vol. 3, pp. 96 f.

6. DODGE, R. Die motorischen Wortvorstellungen. Halle a. S., M. Niemeyer, 1896, pp. 40 and 77.

7. DARWIN, CHAS. The Expression of the Emotions in Man and Animals. New York, D. Appleton & Co., 1873, pp. 273 ff.

8. WUNDT, W. Völkerpsychologie. Leipsic, W. Engelmann, 1900, Vol. 1, Part I, pp. 175 f.

9. LIEBER, F. On the Vocal Sounds of Laura Bridgeman. Smithsonian Contributions to Knowledge, Washington, 1851, Vol. 2, Art 2, pp. 11 f. (Laura wrote her name: Bridgman.)

10. GARNER, R. L. The Speech of Monkeys. New York, Chas. Webster & Co., 1892, pp. 57 ff.

11. FÉRÉ, CHAS. Sensation et mouvement. Paris, F. Alcan, 1887, pp. 102 f.

12. JAMES, W. The Principles of Psychology. New York, Henry Holt & Co., 1890, Vol. 2, pp. 372 and 381.

13. BEARD, G. M. The History of Muscle-Reading. Journal of Science, and Annals of Astronomy, Biology, Geology, etc., London, 1881, Series 3, Vol. 3, p. 558 f.

14. LAURENT, L.   Les procédés des liseurs de pensées.   Journal de psychologie normale et pathologique, Paris, 1905, second year, No. 6, pp. 489 f.

15. GUICCIARDI, G. e G. C. FERRARI.   Il lettore del pensiero " John Dalton."   Rivista sperimentale di Freniatria ecc., Reggio nell' Emilia, 1898, Vol. 24, p. 209.

16. TARCHANOFF, J. de.   Hypnotisme, suggestion et lecture de pensées.   Translated from the Russian by E. Jaubert, second edition.   Paris, G. Masson, 1893, pp. 153 ff.

17. PREYER, W.   Telepathie und Geisterseherei in England.   Deutsche Rundschau, Berlin, 1886, Jahrg. 12, Heft 4, p. 40.

18. SOMMER, R.   Dreidimensionale Analyse von Ausdrucksbewegungen.   Zeitschrift für Psychologie und Physiologie der Sinnesorgane, Leipsic, 1898, Vol. 16, pp. 280 ff.

19. FRENKEL, H.   Des secousses rhythmiques de la tête chez les aortiques et chez les personnes saines.   Revue de Médecine, Paris, 1902, 22nd Year, No. 7, pp. 617 ff.

20. ZONEFF, P. and E. MEUMANN.   Über Begleiterscheinungen psychischer Vorgänge in Atem und Puls.   Philosophische Studien, edited by W. Wundt, Leipsic, 1903, vol. 18, p. 3.

21. MÜLLER, G. E. and A. PILZECKER.   Experimentelle Beiträge zur Lehre vom Gedächtniss.   Zeitschrift fur Psychologie und Physiologie der Sinnesorgane, Leipsic, 1900, Ergänzungsband 1, pp. 58 ff.

22. KRAEPELIN, E.   Der psychologische Versuch in der Psychiatrie. Psychologische Arbeiten, edited by the same, Leipsic, 1895, Vol. 1, pp. 50 ff.

23. AMBERG, E.   Über den Einfluss von Arbeitspausen auf die geistige Leistungsfähigkeit.   Ditto, pp. 374 ff.

24. SHALER, N. S.   Domesticated animals.   London, Smith Elder & Co., 1896, pp. 143 ff.

25. COUPIN, H.   L'esprit des animaux domestiques.   La Revue, Paris, 1903, first quarter, Vol. 44, p. 586.

26. (LEBRUN, P.).   Lettres qui découvrent l'illusion des philosophes sur la baguette, et qui détruisent leurs systèmes.   Paris, J. Boudot, 1696, pp. 239 ff.

27. Notice sur un nouvel instrument, dont Mr. Ritter, membre de l'académie de Munich s'est servi dans les expériences qu'il a récemment faites avec Mr. Campetti etc.   Bibliothèque Brittannique, Sciences et Arts, Geneva, 1807, Vol. 35, p. 91.

28. ZELL, TH. Tierfabeln und andere Irrtümer in der Tierkunde. 2nd edition. Stuttgart, Kosmos (1905), p. 38.

29. THORNDIKE, E. L. Animal Intelligence. Psychological Review, Lancaster, Pa. and New York, 1898, Monograph Supplements, Vol. 2, No. 4, p. 95.

30. VASCHIDE, N. et P. ROUSSEAU. Études expérimentales sur la vie mentale des animaux. Revue scientifique, Paris, 1903, Series 4, Vol. 19, No. 25, p. 782.

31. ETTLINGER, M. Sind die Tiere vernünftig? Hochland, Munich and Kempten, 1904, Jahrg, 2, Heft 2, p. 223.

32. ROMANES, G. J. On the Mental Faculties of the Bald Chimpanzee (Anthropopithecus calvus). Proceedings of the Scientific Meetings of the Zoological Society of London, 1889, pp. 320 f.

33. KINNAMAN, A. J. Mental Life of two Macacus rhesus Monkeys in Captivity. American Journal of Psychology, Worcester, Mass., 1902, Vol. 13, No. 1, pp. 139 ff.

34. HIMSTEDT, FR. and W. A. NAGEL. Versuche über die Reizwirkung verschiedener Strahlenarten auf Menschen- und Tier- augen. Festschrift der Albrecht-Ludwigs-Universität in Freiburg zum 50 jährigen Regierungs-Jubiläum Sr. Konigl. Hoheit des Groszherzogs Friedrich. Freiburg i. Br., C. A. Wagner, 1902, pp. 272 ff.

35. DAHL, F. Naturwissenschaftliche Wochenschrift, Jena, 1905, New series, Vol. 4, No. 48, pp. 767 ff.

36. CORTE, CLAUDIO. Il cavallerizzo. Di nuove dall' auttore stesso corretto ed emendato. Venice, G. Ziletti, 1573, Book 1, Chap. 6, page 8. (I did not have access to the first edition of 1562, cf. Graesse, Trésor de livres rares, 1861, Vol. 2, p. 277.)

37. RIEGEL. Untersuchungen über die Ametropie der Pferde. Monatshefte für praktische Tierheilkunde, Stuttgart, 1904, Bd. 16, Heft 1, pp. 31 ff.

38. BERLIN, R. Über die Schätzung der Entfernungen bei Tieren. Zeitschrift für vergleichende Augenheilkunde, Wiesbaden, 1891, Bd. 7, Heft 1, pp. 5 f.

39. THE SAME. Über ablenkenden Linsen-Astigmatismus und seinen Einfluss auf das Empfinden von Bewegung. Ditto, 1887, Bd. 5, Heft 1, pp. 7 ff.

40. SCHLEICH, G. Das Sehvermögen der höheren Tiere. Tübingen, F. Pietzcker, 1896, p. 24.

41. KÖNIGSHÖFER. Über das Äugen des Wildes. Monatshefte des Allgemeinen Deutschen Jagdschutz-Vereins, Berlin, 1898, Jahrg. 3, No. 17, pp. 250 f.

42. ZÜRN, J. Vergleichend histologische Untersuchungen über die Retina und die Area centralis retinæ der Haussäugetiere. Archiv fur Anatomie und Physiologie, Anatomische Abteilung, Leipsic, 1902, Supplementary volume, pp. 116 ff.

43. HIRSCHBERG, J. Zur vergleichenden Ophthalmoskopie. Archiv fur Anatomie und Physiologie, Physiologische Abteilung, Leipsic, Jahrg. 1882, p. 96.

44. BERLIN, R., see 39, p. 4.

45. THE SAME. Über den physikalisch-optischen Bau des Pferdeauges. Zeitschrift fur vergleichende Augenheilkunde, Leipsic, 1882, Jahrg. 1, Heft 1, p. 32.

46. BAYER, J. Tierärztliche Augenheilkunde. Vol. 5 of the "Handbuch der Tierärztlichen Chirurgie und Geburtshilfe" by J. Bayer und E. Fröhner. Vienna und Leipsic, W. Braumüller, 1900, p. 459.

47. THE SAME. Ditto, p. 475.

48. RIEGEL, see 37, p. 35.

48a. SCHWENDIMANN, F. Untersuchungen über den Zustand der Augen bei scheuen Pferden. Archiv für wissentschaftliche und praktische Tierheilkunde, Berlin, 1903, Bd. 29, Heft 6, p. 566.

48b. BERLIN, R. Refraktion und Refraktionsanomalien von Tieraugen. Tageblatt der 52. Versammulung deutscher Naturforscher und Ärzte in Baden-Baden, 1879, p. 348. See also 45, pp. 28 f. and 39, p. 13.

49. THE SAME, see 39, p. 9.

50. BAYER, J., see 46, pp. 460 f.

51. ZÜRN, J., see 42, p. 114.

52. CHIEVITZ, J. H. Über das Vorkommen der Area centralis retinæ in den vier höheren Wirbeltierklassen. Archiv für Anatomie und Physiologie, Anatomische Abteilung, Leipsic, 1891, Heft 4-6, p. 329.

53. ZÜRN, J., see 42, p. 140.

54. KÖNIGSHÖFER, see 41, pp. 251 ff.

55. TENNECKER, S. v. Bemerkungen und Erfahrungen über den Charakter und das Temperament, sowie über die geistigen Eigenschaften des Pferdes überhaupt. Beiträge zur Natur- und Heilkunde, von Friedrich und Hesselbach, Würzburg, 1825, Vol. 1, pp. 110 f.

56. ZBORZILL, E. Die mnemonische Dressur des Hundes. Berlin, S. Mode (1865), p. 21.

57. MÜLLER, AD. und K. Tiere der Heimat. 3rd Edition, Cassel, Th. Fischer, 1897, Book 1, p. 70.

58. HUTCHINSON, W. N. Dog Breaking. 6th Edition, London, J. Murray, 1876, pp. 105 f.

59. HUGGINS, LADY M. Kepler : a Biography. Cited by Sir J. Lubbock, On the Senses, Instincts, and Intelligence of Animals. London, Kegan Paul, Trench and Co., 1888, pp. 284 f. (The original was published privately and never put on the market. Hence it was not accessible for me.)

60. LUBBOCK, SIR J. Ditto, p. 285.

61. ROUHET, G. L'entraînement complet et expérimental de l'homme avec étude sur la voix articulée, suivi de recherches physiologiques et pratiques sur le cheval. Paris, Libraires associés, and Bordeaux, Feret et fils, 1902, pp. 517 ff.

62. LIPPS, TH. Zur Psychologie der Suggestion. Leipsic, J. A. Barth, 1897, pp. 5 f.

63. ZELL, TH. See 1, pp. 40 f.

64. ZBORZILL, E. See 56, p. 23.

65. BEARD, G. M. Physiology of Mind-Reading. Popular Science Monthly, New York, February 1877. Vol. 10, p. 472. Reprint in the Journal of Science, and Annals of Astronomy, Biology, Geology, etc., London, 1881, Series 3, Vol. 3, p. 418.

66. BABINET. Les tables tournantes au point de vue de la mécanique et de la physiologie. Revue des deux mondes, Paris, 1854, Twenty-fourth year, Vol. 5, pp. 409 f.

67. TOLSTOI, L. N. Anna Karenina.

68. GOLDBECK. Besitzen die Tiere, speziell Hunde, Verstand oder nicht? Deutsche tierärztliche Wochenschrift, Hannover, 1902, Jahrg. 10, No. 20, p. 202.

69. MENAULT, E. L'intelligence des animaux. 4th Edition, Paris, Hachette et Cie., 1872, p. 233.

70. LEBON, G. L'equitation actuelle et ses principes. 3rd Edition, Paris, Firmin-Didot et Cie., 1895, pp. 120 and 288.

71. LOISET, B. Praktischer Unterricht in Kunstdarstellungen mit Pferden. New edition. Stuttgart, Schickhardt u. Ebner, 1884, pp. 69 f. and 98 ff.

72. BAUCHER, F. Dictionnaire raisonné d'équitation. 2nd Edition, Paris, chez l'auteur, 1851, pp. 291 ff.

73. ARNIM, v. Praktische Anleitung zur Bearbeitung des Pferdes an der Longe. 2nd Edition, Leipsic, Zuckschwerdt und Co., 1896, pp. 18 f. and 39 f.

74. MEEHAN, J. The Berlin "Thinking" Horse. Nature, London. 1904, Vol. 70, No. 1825, p. 602.

75. SPOHR. Die Logik in der Reitkunst. Part 2. Pamphlet No. 32 in the Series: "Unsere Pferde." Stuttgart, Schickhardt und Ebner, 1904, p. 29 f.

76. REDDING, T. B. The Intelligence of a Horse. Science, New York, 1892, Vol. 20, No. 500, pp. 133 f.

77. SPOHR. Die naturgemäsze Gesundheitspflege der Pferde. 4th Edition, Hannover, Schmorl u. v. Seefeld Nachf., 1904, p. 164.

78. DECROIX, E. Projet de langage phonétique universel pour la conduite des animaux. Bulletin de la Société nationale d'Acclimatation de France, Paris, 1898, Forty-fourth Year, pp. 241 ff.

79. NOIZET, GÉNÉRAL. Etudes philosophiques. Paris, H. Plon, 1864, Vol. 1, pp. 471 ff.

80. BEARD, G. M. See 65, Vol. 10, p. 471.

81. LEBON, G. See 70, p. 120.

82. FLÜGEL, O. Das Seelenleben der Tiere. 3rd Edition, Langensalza, H. Beyer und Söhne, 1897, pp. 50 f.

83. LANDOIS, H. Über das musikalische Gehör der Pferde. Zeitshrift für Veterinärkunde, Berlin, 1889, Jahrg. 1, No. 6. pp. 237 ff.

84. FOVEAU DE COURMELLES. Les facultés mentales des animaux, Paris, J. B. Baillière et fils, 1890, p. 142.

85. ZÜRN, F. A. Die intellektuellen Eigenschaften (Geist und Seele) der Pferde. Pamphlet 8 of the Series: "Unsere Pferde." Stuttgart., Schickhardt und Ebner, 1899, p. 26.

86. FILLIS, J. Tagebuch der Dressur. Translated from the French by J. Halperson and G. Goebel. Stuttgart, Schickhardt und Ebner, 1906, pp. 322 f.

87. ATHENAEUS. Dipnosophistae. Book 12, 520 c. Edited by G. Kaibel. Leipsic, B. G. Teubner, 1890, Vol. 3, pp. 148 f.

88. AELIANUS, CL. De natura animalium. Book 16, 23. Edited by R. Hercher. Leipsic, B. G. Teubner, 1864, Vol. 1, p. 401.

89. JULIUS AFRICANUS, S. Κεστοί, chapter 14. In: Veterum Mathematicorum Opera. Paris, Typographia Regia, 1693, p. 293.

9c. GUÉNON, A. Influence de la musique sur les animaux et en particulier sur le cheval. (Châlons-sur-Marne), 1898, pp. 83 ff.

91. LÉPINAY. L'hypnotisme chez le cheval. Revue de l'hypnotisme, Paris, 1903, Eighteenth Year, No. 5, pp. 152 f.

92. FILLIS, J. Grundsätze der Dressur und Reitkunst. Translated from the French by G. Goebel. 3rd Edition, Stuttgart, Schickhardt und Ebner, 1905, pp. 10 f.

93. MANOUVRIER, L. Mouvements divers et sueur palmaire consécutifs à des images mentales. Revue philosophique, Paris, 1886, Vol. 22, pp. 204 ff.

94. GASPARIN, CTE A. DE. Des tables tournantes, du surnaturel en général et des esprits. 2nd Edition, Paris, E. Dentu, 1855, Vol. 1, Part 1.

95. RIVERS, W. H. R. and E. KRAEPELIN. Über Ermüdung and Erholung. Psychologische Arbeiten, edited by E. Kraepelin, Leipsic, 1895, Vol. 1, pp. 636 f.

96. (CARPENTER, W. B.). Spiritualism and its Recent Converts. Quarterly Review, London, 1871, Vol. 131, No. 262, p. 312.

97. DARWIN, CHAS. See 7, p. 48.

98. SAINT-ANGE, DE. Cours d'hippologie. 2nd Edition, Paris, chez Dumaine et chez Leneveu and Saumur, chez Mlle. Niverlet et chez Mlle. Dubosse, 1854, Vol. 1, p. 101.

99. FRANZIUS, G. Die Wünschelrute. Zentralblatt der Bauverwaltung, Berlin, 1905, Jahrg. 25, No. 74, pp. 461 f.

100. MÉNESTRIER, CL. FR. La philosophie des images énigmatiques. Lyon, J. Guerrier, 1694, pp. 483 f.

101. (LEBRUN, P.). Histoire critique des pratiques superstitieuses, qui ont séduit les peuples et embarassé les sçavans. Paris (et Amsterdam), 1702, p. 42.

102. AGRICOLA, G. De re metallica libri XII, eiusdem de animantibus subterraneis liber. Basel, Froben, 1556, Book 2, pp. 27 f.

103. SCHOTT, C. Magia universalis naturæ et artis. Würzburg, J. G. Schönwetters Erben, 1659, Part 4, Book 4, p. 430.

104. THE SAME. Physica curiosa, sive mirabilia naturae et artis. Würzburg, 1662, Part 2, Book 12, p. 1532.

105. ZEIDLER, J. G. Pantomysterium, oder das Neue vom Jahre in der Wünschelruthe, etc. Hall in Magdeburg (Halle a. S.), Renger, 1700, Chap. 2. p. 47.

106. BARRETT, W. F. On the so-called Divining Rod, or Virgula Divina. Proceedings of the Society for Psychical Research, London, 1897, Vol. 13, pp. 177 f.

107. THEOPHANES. Chronographia. Paris, Typographia Regia, 1655, pp. 189 f.

108. YOUATT, W. The Dog. London, Ch. Knight and Co., 1845, pp. 108 ff.

109. TARADE, E. DE. Traité de l'élevage et de l'éducation du chien. Paris, E. Lacroix (1866), pp. 113 ff.

110. HACHET-SOUPLET, P. Die Dressur der Tiere. Translated from the French by O. Marschall v. Bieberstein, Leipsic, O. Klemm, 1898, pp. 36 f.

111. LUBBOCK, SIR J. See 59, pp. 280 f.

112. LÉONARD, A. Essai sur l'éducation des animaux, le chien pris pour type. Lille, Leleux, 1842, pp. 81-185.

113. MEEHAN, J. See 74, p. 602.

114. FRANCONI (GÄRTNER). Die Dressur der Kunstpferde. Jahrbuch fur Pferdezucht, Pferdekenntnis, Pferdehandel usw. auf das Jahr 1835, Weimar und Ilmenau, 1835, Jahrg. 11, p. 329.

115. LOISET, B. See 71, p. 130.

116. HACHET-SOUPLET, P. See 110, p. 91.

117. KNICKENBERG, F. Der Hund und sein "Verstand." Cöthen (Anhalt), P. Schettlers Erben, 1905, pp. 129 f.

118. LANG, R. Geheimnisse zur künstlichen Abrichtung der Hunde, revised edition. Augsburg and Leipsic, A. Bäumer, pp. 46 f.

119. FRANCONI (GÄRTNER). See 114, pp. 326 f.

120. TENNECKER, S. v. Erinnerungen aus meinem Leben. Altona, I. F. Hammerich, 1838, Vol. 1, pp. 21 f. (The name of the author is erroneously given on the title page as F. v. Tennecker.)

121. LOISET, B. See 71, p. 132.

122. D—. Über die Abrichtung der kleinen Kunstpferde zu dem Zählen mit dem Fusse, Kopfschütteln und dgl. Zeitung für die Pferdezucht, den Pferdehandel, die Pferdekenntnis usw., Tübingen, 1804, Vol. 4, p. 51.

123. LANG, R. See 118, pp. 52 f.

124. BUFFON, CTE DE, et L. DAUBENTON. Histoire naturelle, générale et particulière. Paris, Imprimerie royale, 1753, Vol. 4, p. 169.